Addicted to the Climb

by Kelley Tyan

ISBN: 979-8-9852151-0-6

Copyright 2021, Kelley Tyan
First Edition: December 7, 2021
Self-Published by Kelley Tyan
Edited & Designed by Ellie Turk

Testimonials

Thanks to my incredible community of friends, clients, and mentors who took time to read Addicted To The Climb early on and share their impression of the book!

Kelley Tyan

Kelley Tyan is amazing! She is a faith-led leader with a wealth of knowledge about fitness. Partner that with a foundation of faith and you've got a leader you can trust. This book is inspiring and transformational. A must read.

-Stefanie Gass
The Stefanie Gass Show

Addicted To The Climb is a powerful read reminding us of the importance having a strong faith and surrounding ourselves with people that not only support us, but light us up as well.

-LeeAnne Hayden
Cancer Survivor/Ostomy Lifer

With so much noise and distractions in today's world, you need a voice that stands out, touches your heart, and gives you the tools you need to break through any barriers to reach your goals. Kelly is that voice. Her heartfelt stories strengthen your faith and inspire hope! I loved every story and every page.

-Amberly Lago
Bestselling Author of True Grit and Grace and TEDx Speaker

Addicted To The Climb is a gift to everyone that feels they are lacking faith and not living to their highest potential in their health life but don't know the steps to start taking.

-Lindsey Schwartz
Powerhouse Women Co.

Kelley is a powerhouse, faith-filled leader! This woman has a true calling on her life! If you are looking for someone to call you higher into the person you know God has called you to be & take your faith & fitness to the next level this is your GIRL!! It is an honor to be led and learn from her and all her expertise, wisdom & life experiences. I can not wait to dive into Addicted To The Climb - I know this will be a new favorite of mine & one that I will share with my very own clients

-Brook Thomas
CEO & Founder of LIVE OUT LOUD

Kelley Tyan shows readers how to take control of their lives and achieve their greatest aspirations. Her perspective on marrying physical fitness and spiritual well-being to create life-changing results is an inspiration to all those seeking courage and optimism.

-Karyn Polito

Addicted To The Climb is a gift to everyone that feels they are not living to their potential, but don't know what steps to take to start living their best life. With faith as the cornerstone, Kelley helps the reader see that anything is possible for them if they believe.

Heather Monahan

Top 50 Keynote Speaker in the World, 2022

If you've opened this book, you're hungry for inspiration to take the next - or first - step in your journey. I pray that through these stories, you become Addicted to the Climb of life again.

Kelley

Dedication

For my incredible family:

Tony my husband, who is my rock and true love.
Taylor and Tony, you are God's masterpieces, given to me, to lead and guide you through life. I love you all with my whole heart and thank you for believing in me.

This is a gift to you to always remember to keep on climbing no matter what you face.

I dedicate this book to my mother, Norma, who will forever be my biggest inspiration, my angel, and my #1 cheerleader in life.

You taught me how to love unconditionally, showed me how to build a strong faith in God without wavering, and how to keep climbing upwards through life, even through the storms. Even as you lived in constant pain throughout your life, you were a true living example of love, peace, joy, and hope in this tumultuous world.

My mother realized at a young age that the mind is a battlefield, and God is the only one that can keep us grounded without fear, angst, and defeat. She taught me that no matter what we face, He will make a way. Even if we can't see it, she taught me there's no sense in giving up.

Her smile lit up any and every room she entered and she was a true light to anyone that ever met her. I am the blessed one to be able to have called her mother, and for that, I am forever grateful.

I have realized and know for sure that there is only one thing you can count on in this life: There is always going to be another mountain to climb. It is how you decide to take the first step.

♡ Kelley

Kelley Tyan has worked with thousands of women as a transformation coach, empowering them to pursue health in their bodies, and souls. She is a 4x national bikini champion, founder and host of Addicted To The Climb podcast, and a breast cancer survivor. She empowers women through the lessons she has learned by overcoming adversities in her own life.

Through all the adversities she has faced throughout her life, Kelley has become addicted to the climb of faith. Her mission has always been to reach and transform one woman a day. Are you ready to climb higher in your life? Kelley is the woman who can help you get there!

@kelleytyan
@kelleytyan
kelleytyan.com

9

Table of Contents

Want to connect with Kelley and her community of women who are Addicted To The Climb?

We will be reading along and sharing encouragement in the Facebook group **Faith, Fuel and Fitness with Kelley Tyan**

Find Kelley's podcast, **Addicted To The Climb** with new episodes weekly on all streaming platforms.

You can also learn more about Kelley and her services at **www.kelleytyan.com**

Foreward

Faith-Fueled stories that will help you break through your own barriers that have been holding you back. They will give you hope and courage to keep going and stay on the climb, no matter what happens around you.

Faith is the backbone of who I am today. I had such a strong spiritual upbringing, and I am so thankful I had a mother and father who never gave up on me even in my darkest times. Faith always gave me the courage to keep on climbing upwards even when I couldn't see the road ahead. After all, the definition of faith is to believe and trust even when you can't see.

Learning how to fully rely on God for everything in my life did not happen overnight. I resisted Him at times and put my faith aside because I felt I could handle things all on my own. However, watching my mother grow up with her Bible in hand at all times put an imprint on my heart. It is something I will cherish forever, even if I did make fun of her at times.

I always wondered what she was reading or why she was reading it so much. Now it makes sense to me. In fact, it makes so much sense that I wanted to take her place where she left off.

This book is made up of 3 sections: faith, fuel, and fitness.

She passed suddenly early in the morning in May 2017. I was there picking her up for a doctor appointment. My life turned upside down quickly, but thankfully I had my faith to fall back on.

Those are the moments to fully rely on God to carry you through. In everything I do, I acknowledge Him, who gives me just enough strength to face my fears, conquer my battles and keep on climbing. He wants to do this for you too. He wants you to cling to His promises that are spread throughout these personal stories, and that is what faith is all about.

Throughout a successful health and fitness career, I've had to constantly work on keeping my faith strong against negative thoughts that have tried to tear me down. Body shaming and negative body image are things I've struggled with, and unfortunately, too many of us suffer from this. Having a strong faith is the only way I can release these thoughts to God. It is my prayer that you will learn to do the same. I want you to feel empowered and energized about God's unconditional love towards you.

Having a deep faith doesn't always mean life is going to be easier. It just means that you are not alone on your journey!

Knowing and believing this settles my soul. It brings me peace and rest, even when everything around me seems to be crumbling.

I pray that your faith grows stronger and you feel empowered to stay on your own journey to keep on climbing, no matter what you face.

These stories are written to encourage you in your walk with God, increase your faith, activate your fitness, and to give you grace. You don't have to feel you should live up to some perfect expectation that the world may put on you.

God is ready to *bless you* in ways you've never even dreamed of. Are you ready to *trust* Him and *let Him* take the lead?

A Note From Kelley

Whether you want to get more fit in your mind or body, or take your negative thoughts out of your head and put God at the forefront, my prayer is that these stories will fire you up! I want them to fuel you each day and motivate you to keep showing up. Every morning when you get out of bed, you have a choice to either take charge of your thoughts, or let the world around you do it for you.

You were born to win and God wants you to shine your light in this world and not let others dim it. You were created to live a healthy, happy, and fit life, even through obstacles and setbacks. Without them, there is no growth.

Let these pages remind you of who you are and Whose you are, while guiding you along your journey and climb.

Each section will help you increase your faith, increase your fitness and strength, and fuel your mind through repetition of affirmations and prayers. May God bless you as you read each page and give you the supernatural strength for each day ahead.

Getting Started...

For the first 10 days, I want you to begin
your day with these 3 journal prompts:

Today I am *staying on the climb* and committing to:

_____

_____

_____

Today, _____

is a *non-negotiable,* and I will stay committed.

I promise myself that *today* I will be

_____

_____

_____

_____

_____

_____

_____

_____

_____

_____

_____

_____

_____

_____

_____

_____

You are what you repeatedly do.

- Aristotle

Faith

Faith Like A Mustard Seed

Introduction

Who or what do you rely on when the going gets tough? I have realized over the years that faith is the only thing we can really rely on. After all, at the end of the day, people will disappoint and excitement for things fades quickly.

Friends will disappoint, a spouse will disappoint, and sometimes, we even disappoint ourselves. This is all part of life. However, when you start to develop a deeper faith, your mindset can change drastically. Even through challenging circumstances, faith can see you through when no one else can or is available.

Through the stories I am sharing, faith has not only boosted my moods, but it has also brought me through my hardest moments. God tells us that even if you have faith as small as a mustard seed, you can move mountains! Doesn't that fire you up right at this moment? I am encouraging you to start developing a deeper faith in God and watch how differently life will be even through the storms.

But those who wait on the Lord will find new strength. They will fly high on wings like eagles. They will run and not grow weary. They will walk and not faint.

- Isaiah 40:31

Patiently Waiting Or Waiting Patiently?

Do you consider yourself a patient person? For example, when you want something, do you do it immediately, or do you wait for the right timing?

I despise waiting! Especially when it is something I desire deeply. I'm not talking about impulse shopping or buying that thing that will make you happy in an instant then fade away.

This verse is speaking about waiting for the Lord to direct our steps and paths in life.

Maybe you are waiting for the right man or woman to show up and you are being impatient. Maybe you want to jump into a new venture or business idea. Or, maybe you've tried to eat clean and exercise, but you didn't see results in the timely manner that you wanted to.

Do you give up easily and go back to your old ways, or do you wait for God to show you the next steps?

This verse is directly speaking to that answer and feeling. It is saying that waiting on the Lord for His direction will give you clarity and then you will be able to fly like an eagle.

When I first started writing this book a few years ago, I wanted it to be all done in an instant. There were many times I had to sit back and pray, being patient in the process. This verse can be a complete game changer in your life if you apply it directly to your impatience. Pray. Wait. Then, watch God work his hands in your life without rushing through the process.

I realize that waiting is hard. It is even hard to wait for that 1 minute while something is in the microwave! Right? Every time I choose to wait on God, the end results have always been in my favor. When I try to speed through the process and do it my way, which is rushed, there always seems to be more challenges that I face.

Which area in your life are you trying to rush through right now? What are you seeking right now that you can give to God instead?

Write out a new prayer so you can relax in God and rely on His strength. He will help you accomplish the task He wants you to finish.

Dear Lord Jesus, help me to be patient while You are making a clear path for the steps I need to take every single day. I want to walk in Your ways and not mine. Help me to walk in Your strength, so that I can fly with wings like eagles and never grow weary along the journey.

I can do all this through Christ who gives me strength.

- Phillippians 4:13

The Fitness Competition

Have you ever heard this verse before or even said it to yourself, but you really didn't believe it?

I knew this verse from when I was a little girl, but it only went in one ear and out the other. These words really came to life for me at my first fitness competition. Can you believe that? Out of all places!

As I was getting ready to walk across the stage, I started trembling, my knees were buckling, and I thought I was going to pass out. (That may have been from not eating enough or drinking water that day, but that's another story). All of a sudden, I remembered my mother always saying to me, "I can do all things through Christ who gives me strength."

At that very moment, I put my shoulders back and walked out on stage saying this over and over again until the very end of the show. I probably said it 100X in a row. I never stopped, and I had a peace and calmness that came over my whole being. It was supernatural, and I will never forget it.

The Lord went ahead and blessed me to become a 4X national fitness champion. He brought me endless opportunities to speak, be in magazines, and start spreading my faith and fitness message. Even through difficult times, and even when you're feeling anxious, this verse can quiet your mind in an instant.

Have you ever been so afraid to the point you couldn't breathe? Or anxiety crept up inside you, and your body felt frozen? Maybe you have had an experience different than being in a fitness show. Regardless of the situation, I know that when you ask God to enter the picture, everything calms down. He will give you the strength you need at that very moment.

There are going to be many times when we feel weak in life. However, hanging on to this verse can change the trajectory of your day and the way you look at your situation. God wants you to be fearless, and he wants you to remember that His strength is greater than yours alone.

I have Phillippians 4:13 on my home gym wall to remind myself of who I am and Whose I am. Write this verse down and repeat it over and over. Soon, you will begin to see yourself differently when you face fears. Although they may come, they will not conquer. Draw your strength from God, and He will make a way for you.

In what areas do you tend to live in fear? How are you going to approach a situation next time fear enters your mind? What are you going to do next time that fear tries to grip you and take over your thoughts?

Repeat this verse today as many times as you need, and watch how differently your outcome can be.

Thank You Lord for the promise that You gave me to prosper me and give me a future that is hopeful. I am opening my heart to you right now to lead me down the path you have for me.

Truly I tell you, if you have faith as small as a mustard seed, you can say to this mountain, 'Move from here to there,' and it will move. Nothing will be impossible for you.

– Matthew 17:20

faith

My Mother, Norma

God tells us that if we have faith as tiny as a mustard seed, we can move mountains. Being human, we are constantly battling negative thoughts in our minds.

After my mother passed, I was on the edge of despair. I was lost, lonely, and scared. After all, she was my partner in crime, my mentor, my best friend, and she possessed all the qualities of a superhuman in Christ. She taught me everything she knew about God, love, marriage, being a mother...and without her being here anymore, I just didn't think I could go on alone.

Being an only child and having her as my best friend was such a blessing. I never took it for granted. I remember crying for the umpteenth night in a row (is that even a word?), and the thought of having faith like a mustard seed entered my mind. I sat upright on my floor in my living room corner where I spent most nights crying, and decided to hold on to that verse for a moment. I wanted to have faith that I would be ok, and I started to remember what my mother taught me. Then I started to believe it.

Have you ever felt so lonely, broken in your spirit, or grief stricken that you've lost all your faith? Maybe you lost faith in yourself or in someone else that hurt you. Or maybe you even experienced a death.

Hang on to this verse, and know that you can move mountains to come back stronger than you ever were before. You just need to have faith as tiny as a mustard seed.

After that night, I made a decision to turn my mother's death around in my head. I chose to count it as a blessing that I got to spend 43 years with her. How blessed was I?

In order to move forward in a situation such as this, it comes down to making one decision to have faith. Think of that tiny mustard seed!

How can you turn around your circumstances right now? Where are you lacking faith?

Find a quiet place, and let God show you how real He is, and how He wants to help you overcome your fears and rebuild your faith step by step. You are born to win and to move mountains. Never forget that.

Prayer

Dear Lord Jesus, thank You for showing me that I can move mountains with even a small amount of faith.

Faith

For I know the plans I have for you declares the Lord, plans to prosper you, and not to harm you, plans to give you hope and a future.

- *Jeremiah 29:11*

God's Plans

This verse has been a complete game changer in my life over the last few years. Being an entrepreneur and often being alone, there have been many times I have felt hopeless about my business.

Negative thoughts would come in my mind like these: "Who do you think you are to write a book?" "No one is going to buy your programs; stop wasting time." "Why are you even doing this?"...These thoughts would stop me dead in my tracks and ruin my day at times, until I really held onto this verse.

I will never forget the night someone said to me, "You seem so busy all the time. Isn't this just a hobby? Why are you wasting so much time being so busy, and for what? It's not like you are making a million dollars!"

This shook me to my core. I think I cried for 3 hours and told myself I am stopping what I am doing. After all, no one will even care or remember me. I decided I was just going to be a mom, focus on my network marketing company, and serve the clients I already had. Then I went to bed, exhausted and drained, ready to announce my termination to anyone who cared on my social media accounts.

God had another plan…..He said, "NO NO NO. The

lives you are touching are far greater than any monetary value, and you are doing work for Me!" When I woke up, I checked my inboxes and there was a message:

"Hi Kelley! I just wanted to say how grateful I am for you and all that you are doing for us! I am grateful for the Bible study you lead on Mondays, and I know I am stronger because of them. I just wanted to tell you how much I appreciate you."

I started crying again. God was speaking to me in that moment, confirming the work I am doing for Him. I put my pride aside and prayed. I opened to Jeremiah 29:11 and read it over and over again. I knew God had a plan for me and I must continue His work, because there are lives that will be transformed and healed through it.

Here's the deal: When you are praying for something and God acts on it, listen! I promise He will follow through, even if the path seems hazy or unknown. Since that message, I have received many more affirmations of the work that I am doing, and I can't thank Jesus enough for showing up when I needed Him. What if I had quit what I started?

Have you ever felt hopeless in your career or not sure if you are on the right track? What if God really has a plan for you right now, and you shut Him out?

God has a plan for you, and He wants to see you succeed. You cannot give up on your dreams, especially the ones He has placed on your heart. Fear will try to enter, but God is more powerful than all your fears.

His plan is to prosper you and not harm you, regardless

of your current situation. Even when you are facing difficulties, you must keep going and not give up. You were born on purpose, for a purpose. If you don't know what your purpose is, now is time to draw closer to God and ask Him to direct your steps. The closer you get to God, the more He will reveal Himself to you.

When you make time for him, get ready for bigger and better things to come into your life. You can't expect God to show up if you are not showing up for Him.

How are you going to start showing up for God differently today? Where in your day can you spend more time with him? How are you going to draw closer to God today so you can allow Him to work in you?

Prayer

Thank You Lord for the promise that You gave me to prosper me and give me a future that is hopeful. I am opening my heart to you right now to lead me down the path you have for me.

God is in the midst of her; she shall not be moved; God will help her when morning dawns.

- *Psalm 46:5*

The Diagnosis

One night I was driving home with my parents. We had just visited a dear friend who was in the hospital with a coma. As we were driving, my dad told me the news that he was diagnosed with a rare blood cancer that day. Immediately, my body went into shock.

After all, my dad was the healthiest man I knew from the minute I was born. I can never even remember him having a cold. He ran anywhere from 3 - 8 miles a day for the last 40 years. He was strong in his body and his mind, so this news was out of nowhere, to say the least.

I immediately had 2 choices as I drove home alone. I could cry and say "why?" or, I could rely on God's strength to get me and my family through this. Having fear of the future can stop a person dead in their tracks. It will keep them stuck, depressed, and full of anxiety. Sometimes it's hard to break free. However, you can clothe yourself in God's righteousness and promises.

The future is unknown, and to worry only causes more grief and sorrow. Nothing good can come from worry, and it's like a web that can tangle us. I had to put all my trust that God will make a way and take care of my father. Although it was not easy, I had way more peace doing it that way then trying to put the burden all on my shoulders.

Are you in the midst of uncertainty right now? Are you fearful of the future or how you will move forward? Are you trying to control the future when you know deep down that it is unknown?

Write this verse down and meditate on it daily. Use it to reassure yourself of God's promise that He loves you and will take care of you.

Your trust has to come from that promise in order to move forward.

Giving up control and letting God take over is a feeling of freedom that only He can bring.

Prayer

Heavenly Father, I am giving You all my burdens right now. I am clothing myself with Your strength so You can guard my heart and release all my fears and worries in this very moment. Thank You for being a good, good Father.

_____

_____

_____

_____

_____

_____

_____

_____

_____

_____

_____

_____

_____

_____

_____

_____

_____

_____

Jesus answered her, "If you knew the gift of God and who it is that asks you for a drink, you would have asked Him and He would have given you living water."

– John 14:10

The Living Water

Have you ever felt so thirsty, but then realized that there is no water anywhere to be found? All you want to do is quench your thirst. More than thirst, have you ever been stuck in a situation that you have been trying to get out of for months or maybe even years?

In both of these situations, you have a longing for something: A drink of water, or a change that needs to be made in life. I understand that the two of these examples are extremely different besides the feeling of thirst and the longing to change …

God tells us in John 4 that when we face difficulties in life, or when we are grasping for something, He wants to fill our cup with His living water. He wants to quench our thirst in every single way if we choose to ask him for help.

There have been many times in my business when I felt so thirsty for more, and I thought I was ready to take on more. However, God has shown me different plans. He wanted to slow me down so I could seek Him first and drink from His cup, not my own.

Sometimes we need to slow down so God can fill us up with his peace, joy, love, and living water that will do more than just quench our thirst. There are so many things that the world cannot give us but God can. Today,

I want you to fill up on His love alone and drink from His cup. Watch how fulfilling this can be when you trust in Him and let Him lead your steps.

Prayer

Lord, fill me up with love today so that I will not be thirsty for anything that is not of You. I pray that You will fill my family with the same peace You are giving me right now.

Trust in the Lord with all your heart and lean not on your own understanding; in all your ways submit to Him, and He will make your paths straight.

- Proverbs 3:5-6

Wait For The Green Light To Go

Trust is a hard thing to do, especially when you cannot see the future. I love this verse, because it proves that every time I try to do things my own way, I mess them up.

Like the time I was arguing with my daughter and trying to make decisions for her. She was a young adult, and had become more independent. When I went to God with the situation, He showed me that being a mother is not about making decisions for my child, but it is about guiding them in the best way they should go. They are human beings who want to spread their wings.

God had to remind me of that to keep our relationship close. If He hadn't, I may have pushed her further away from me. I wanted to take control of the situation, but I realized that in doing so, I was shutting God out. When I let Him in and asked Him to intervene by helping me say the right words, things immediately changed, and our conversation changed for the better.

When I lean on God for His direction, things go much more smoothly. God wants us to rely on Him in these situations and in ALL situations.

Have you ever forced something to happen in your life

that you wish you hadn't? In every major decision you are faced with, ask God what He thinks first. Pray about it before you dive in alone, and then trust that He will guide you in the best way possible.

Whether you are single and wishing for a partner, you have kids and want them to get into a school or college, have a financial problem you desperately want to be solved, or you just need a parking space LOL, (my mother prayed about this often), try leaning in more to God. Let Him take the wheel. Doesn't it feel so good and freeing to know that God is in the driver's seat and you can be His passenger?

Just knowing that He can steer you in the right direction, and that He wants you to succeed, takes the burden off your shoulders immediately. What a great feeling that is!

When I pray for God to lead my path and direct my steps, it's amazing how a new thought or idea will pop in my head. I call these downloads from God. It is almost like I am at a stop light, and the light turns green, telling me to go.

Try to pause before you make an important decision or even any decision. Pray that it is led by God, and wait for the light to turn green. Then go! This is exactly how it happened with my daughter. Because of that experience, I have learned to let God lead the way.

_____

*Thank You Lord for showing me the path
You want me to take and making a way for
me today and tomorrow.*

Be strong and courageous. Do not be terrified; do not be discouraged, for the Lord your God will be with you wherever you go.

– Joshua 1:9

Why Not Choose To Be Strong and Courageous?

Jumping into something new is always a bit terrifying in some sort of way. This verse gives me the confidence to just go and do it, especially if it is God led.
My dreams have always circled around gathering large groups of women together. I envision empowering, inspiring, and motivating them to become their best selves in mind, body, and spirit. Even as far back as I can remember as a little girl, I loved gathering different groups of girls together and making new friends.

When the thought came to me about putting on a women's empowerment event, I immediately picked up the phone and called five women who I admired very much. I knew I wanted them to be part of this. One of them was our lieutenant governor, and she immediately said yes.

As fearful as I was to start making the calls and organizing this from the bottom, I said this Bible verse 100X a day. I was terrified at first, because I never put on such a big event and, of course, I wanted it to be perfect. As it was all coming together, I leaned in on God's promise that he was with me from the beginning to the end.

It was called Level Up Boston, and there were over 100 women who showed up. I'll never forget how proud and courageous I felt when it ended. I was so overwhelmed with how God gave me the courage to keep on going.

Even when I wasn't sure tickets would sell or if anyone would show up, God strengthened me. The only thing I could rely on was that once I placed this event in His hands, He would show up bigger and better than I could imagine. Lives were going to be changed and transformed, and that was God's plan from the start. He was with me through the whole process. Guess what? That is the God you can trust and rely upon too, especially when you want to give up.

Stay tuned for bigger and better things to come because I want to see your beautiful face in person at the next one!

When the fear takes over and you feel weak, I want you to recite this verse over and over. After all, why wouldn't you want to feel strong and courageous if that is what God wants you to be? You may still have to go through obstacles, but the calming presence of God will help you along the way. He will keep you moving forward.

Whether you are starting something new in your career, a new relationship, or a new health journey, remind yourself that you are strong and courageous. God is right there holding your hand. Let those words ease your mind right now, in this very moment, because you are one brave and mighty child of the King.

Lord, fill me up with love today so that I will not be thirsty for anything that is not of You. I pray that You will fill my family with the same peace You are giving me right now.

She is clothed with strength and dignity, and she laughs with no fear of the future.

- Proverbs 31:25

The Halo Cast

Have you ever felt like you were stuck inside a prison in your mind and body at the same time?

Well, this nightmare became a reality for my mother in 1986. She was told she would need to be in a halo cast for six months because her neck was so unstable.

The thought of being paralyzed from the neck down was unimaginable for us. There was no question: She had no choice.

I'll never forget when she came home from the hospital that day. Have you ever even seen a halo cast? To give you an idea, it looks like something in a horror movie they use to torture a person.

It was like she was stuck inside four prison walls with 4 straight long bars around her head. These bars were held up by nails that were screwed in her skull. It was and extremely hard thing to see, because you would just want to cry for her.

However, she lived through this period in her life with grace and a smile for six months straight. I am not exaggerating; she was beautiful even through the pain. You could actually see Jesus shining through her at times. You might be wondering how?

For me, seeing this and being in 6th grade brought up many emotions: fear and pain to say the least. I didn't talk about it much with anyone because I was just a kid and we didn't talk about serious things to each other.

I just knew that if my mother was smiling and had an incredible outlook and attitude about her situation, I could do the same. She made us all feel at ease, even if she wasn't at ease herself. She never said a word about it. Instead, she just did her best every single day.

There were times I cried inside because I felt so bad, but

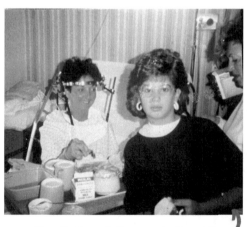

Hey, that's me! Can you believe it?

something always told me she would be ok. I know now
that it was Jesus paving the way.

Looking back and remembering the whole ordeal brings
me to tears, even to this very day. I could easily ask God
why? She was only in her late 20's, and she was just trying
to enjoy life with her husband and only child.

However, I know that God was pruning her to be one
of His soldiers and disciples. He wanted to show others, including myself, that with a deep faith they can get
through anything.

When you have a strong faith built on solid ground, you
can weather the storms better while getting through
them with more peace. The pain is still real, and it certain-
ly stings. But there is a peace that surpasses all understanding. I watched this throughout my mothers whole
life.

Surgery after surgery, new pains appeared in her body
every week. It could get really exhausting for many, but
my mother kept her head up. Her eyes were always fo-
cused on Jesus, and she never wavered in her faith.

I always wondered how she got through the death of her
parents. She lost her parents only 18 months apart, and
then she lost three of her very best girlfriends all in the
same time frame. On top of this deep loss, she was suffering with a disease that was eating up her physical body
on a daily basis. Now I know how she did it.

She carried a peace deep inside her heart because
Jesus was real and she knew He would always carry
her through. When you have an unwavering faith, you'll

become unshakable. Even though the pain is extreme at times, you will learn how to walk through the fires and not get burned. That is the faith I witnessed growing up, and I cling to it every single day.

Your situation might be extremely difficult right now, but there's a God who will help you through it if you let Him.

Never give up on yourself or let your situation grip you like a stronghold. Instead, let God turn your weakness into strength, and allow Him to take control of your thoughts in your suffering. In our humanness we are weak, but in Him, we are strong.

Which way do you prefer to be?

The Proverbs verse above completely captivates who my mother was. We are all capable of faith such as this. It is a choice on our part. My mother paved the way for me and for all those she touched.

Today is the day to let go of fear, worry, and defeat. God wants to lead you down a road filled with strength, love, and peace. The question is, will you let Him?

Lord Jesus, I am inviting You in my situation and life. Only You know the outcome of my circumstances. I am giving You all my fears, worries, and anxieties because I am tired of holding on to them. Give me the strength to get through this day. I am thanking You for it.

Forgetting what is behind and straining toward what is ahead, I press on toward the goal to win the prize for which God has called me heavenward in Christ Jesus.

— Proverbs 31:25

Pressing On Toward The Goal

How many times do you rehearse the problems of your past? How often do you feel shameful and guilty about things you have done or moments you have wasted?

Have you ever heard the phrase, "Don't look back, you are not going that way!?"

Every time I look back and feel I could have done more, or that I should have done things differently, it brings on feelings of sadness, hopelessness, and guilt.

There have been many days where I have sat in misery about my past. I question why I chose to do the things I did, or why I didn't take a different route. The list can be endless as well as tiring.

I know many mothers struggle with "mom guilt." That phrase has been tearing mothers apart, because they feel they cannot keep up with their neighbor.

If you are a mother right now, just know that YOU ARE ENOUGH, and wherever you are on your journey with your children, God is right there with you. If you are feeling guilty in some way, remember that you are only one woman! Allow the Lord to help you strengthen your mind.

Living in the past defeats everything, and God tells us this in the Bible.

What you have or have not done yesterday is over. Today is a new day to start again! Thank God you woke up this morning to have another chance at it all again.

God has created you on purpose for a purpose, and that means looking ahead and not backwards at any and all mistakes you might have made.

I know that death can bring up a lot of guilt for many people because once a loved one passes, guilt of not doing enough or saying the right things can set in. It happens to me at times when I think about my mother.

Did you know that God can cleanse you from these feelings and help you move forward so you can keep your eye on the prize ahead?

When you are growing your faith, your confidence in yourself is also growing. God wants you to let go of what doesn't work or isn't working at the moment, and keep pressing on forward. This allows us to find new ways to approach different areas of life. Throughout our health journey, God does not want you looking back on all your mistakes. This is because he Has called you to accomplish greater things if you keep moving forward.

Maybe you have gained weight and lost weight year after year. From now on, use those moments and thoughts as an awakening in your spirit to work hard. This way you will never go back to feeling guilty and less confident.

Pressing on toward the goal means you don't give up on yourself, because God will never give up on you. Start seeking lessons rather than dwelling on loss or guilt. Your rewards will be great if you keep on climbing.

Prayer

Lord Jesus, give me the desire and the motivation so I can keep moving forward towards my goals. Strengthen my mind and spirit every morning when I wake up, so I can conquer the day with You and take positive action steps. Help me to forgive myself of any negative thinking that has hindered me in the past so I can and will keep pressing on.

Do not be anxious about anything, but in every situation, by prayer and petition, with thanksgiving, present your requests to God.

- *Philippians 4:6*

The Lies We Tell Ourselves

Every time I would get ready to speak at an event, I would panic and get extremely anxious before I would open my mouth. I would feel my heart racing as if I was having a heart attack!

Have you ever felt like this? Maybe you are not a speaker, but have you ever gotten yourself so worked up that you needed to take big deep breaths to calm yourself down? Did that even work? What do you do in these situations?

I remember organizing my first large women's event in Boston. I had the Lieutenant Governor as well as some top influencers speaking at it. Before I got on stage, I thought I was going to get physically sick.

Right then and there, I knew I could not go on stage feeling that way. Immediately, I began to pray and beg Jesus to pour his peace over me. I prayed for Him to take away those anxious thoughts and feelings that were trying to disrupt my mind and cause me such distress.

I knew that being anxious was not what God wanted, and I knew He could help me if I asked. This verse's clear instructions, "do not be anxious about anything," played over and over in my mind.

That verse is a command from God. It is not a question

or a thought. I took it to heart that day and immediately took control of my thoughts.

I want you to know something: Thoughts are just thoughts. We have thousands of them each day. Do you realize that when you keep those negative thoughts circling around in your mind, letting them fester, that you are creating more stress and damage than you realize?

I truly believe this is avoidable, and I want you to take me up on it next time you feel anxious, fearful, or worried.

I have learned over the years and through many experiences to begin to pray without ceasing until the negative feelings fade away.

If you are a parent, you have probably felt some kind of worry or fear about your child at one point. The question is, are you letting that fear and anxiety take over so it is becoming your norm to feel that way?

Being a mother myself, especially with teenagers that drive, that worry can cause real stress. The Bible clearly tells us that those feelings do not come from God. When you really have faith that God's word is the truth, read that verse and watch how He can transform your thoughts and mind.

This may take some time, so please be patient and let Him do His work in you. You are worthy, and you are royalty. Let that sink in. From now on, wrap your head around what God says He can do, not the lies your mind tries to tell you.

Lord, thank You for Your command to not be anxious about anything and to consistently pray when in distress. Even when the nervousness, anxiousness, fear, or panic start to creep in, I am giving these feelings to You so I can be freed of them. Take them from me and swap them with Your love, comfort, and peace. Thank You!

Fuel

Be still and know that I am God.

- Psalm 46:10

Introduction

Where does your fuel source come from at the start of your days? What fires you up to get to work on time or get to the gym? Does it come from the Bible? Social media? The news on TV? I have changed the way I do things when I wake up. Fueling up first thing in the morning on God is the only way I can make it through a day.

When I think about the word "fuel," there are feelings and thoughts that come up such as excitement, motivation, achievement, nourishment, supply, and fire. Where do you get your fuel from?

Within the last couple years, I have started the morning with a new routine. This was not always the way it was for me. For many years, I would fuel up on TV first thing in the morning by watching the news, and then I would scroll on my phone.

When I look back, I was always comparing myself to others on social media. Then, I would see sad stories on the news that either made me cry or got me really upset with the media! What the heck? I hated starting my day off like that!

I knew something had to change, because my outlook on the day ahead was always the same. I needed a fresh start and to feel rejuvenated first thing in the morning.

Looking back, I remember my mother always sitting at her kitchen table reading her Bible with notes all over the table. In my head I thought, " I could never just sit in the morning; I'm way too busy to be that still."

Now, I've taken over where she left off! There are mornings when I plan to sit just 10-15 minutes and end up reading over an hour! Plus taking notes! Quiet mornings with God have been a blessing, and my life has transformed from these moments.

Just like a car drives better when filled up with gasoline, my mind and soul think better when I fuel up on God before the chaos of the day begins. You might be thinking, "I don't have time." I always thought the same thing too! But when I make time for God and allow him to fill me up with his daily messages, I always end up with more time than I even need.

I decided to make a change. Instead of watching the news, I chose to fuel up by reading my Bible and letting God take the wheel of the day ahead. Of course, you have to have a plan.

Preparing your day, whether it is what you will eat or how you will move your body, is a must. Fueling up on nutritious,God-made food is the only way your body can work at its best. How do you want to feel at the end of each day? This is a question that needs to be answered in the beginning of the week, before the days get away from you.
 Preparing and planning your menu is the key to good health and feeling incredible in your body. Your mood comes from the foods you eat, so be mindful of how you fuel up. This is especially important first thing in the

morning.

Your mood also comes from the fuel you consume: TV, media, social platforms, and your own inner circle. These are things you must evaluate right now if you are looking to grow in a different way or head in a new and improved direction.

This section is going to give you daily fuel to fire you up so you can live your healthiest and happiest life with God by your side. Remember, you are never alone, so rely on Him and trust in Him. He will fuel you up in the best way ever if you let Him lead your heart.

There must be a spiritual renewing of your thoughts and minds.

- Ephesians 4:23

Your New Hashtag, #revengemind

Do you ever sit and think yourself to death? I mean, think to the point where you are exhausted because your thoughts are so negative, degrading, small, and even wicked about yourself?

Those are the kind of thoughts I have had to battle with in the past. Thank You Jesus for showing up and teaching me how to handle them! Now, I am so excited to teach you how to handle them too. I know you battle with negative thinking. You are human, and studies have shown that we have on average 6,200 thoughts each day.

How many of those thoughts do you think are full of negativity? Fear? Turmoil? Unworthiness? Since there's a whole lotta thinking going on, I want to share some good news: God CAN and WILL set you free from this battle with thoughts He didn't give you.

My inner dialogue was downright dirty for a very long time. Here are a few examples of thoughts I have had to battle with in the past; maybe you can relate to them too:

"Why would I ever create a podcast, because no one will ever listen to it anyways?" "You do not have as many followers as she does, so why would anyone want you as their coach or buy anything from you?" "You are going to look like a fool writing a book because no one even knows you."

After my mother passed away, I also had to deal with all the vicious thoughts that the devil tried to fill my mind with. "Don't let your children go anywhere, they are not safe." "Your father is not going to make it through his treatments, and he could die too."

Let me stop right there because this list could go on and on. I want to be honest. There were moments that I was so afraid to let my children leave the house, because I was crippled with fear that something bad was going to happen to them.

I felt so tormented in my mind about all my loved ones, because I was so afraid to lose them. This was eating me up inside, and I couldn't take it anymore. Even though I always stayed in prayer in those moments, it was a fight against myself.

Everything changed for me when this one thought happened, and I know it was a complete download from God Himself!! #revengemind!

It was around the time when the show Revenge Body was on TV. If you are not familiar with it, it was based on people taking revenge on friends or family members who had put them down and made fun of them in the past. The main character would get on an exercise and nutrition program to get in the best shape of their life mentally and physically. They would prove how great they could be and feel.

As my own negative thoughts were constantly creeping in, I decided to start taking revenge on them. #Revenge-Mind means taking your negative thoughts and getting angry immediately at them. It means stopping them dead in their nasty little tracks before they start snowballing into a massive mess. I have even opened up a window in the car or at home, and "tossed" them out!

Here's the deal, you are a child of God so that means you were created extremely YOUnique.

What words are you fueling yourself up on a daily basis? I used to tear my body apart and it was all wasted energy and exhausting. I prayed so hard that God would let me see myself the way he sees me and although it has been a slow process, I accepted his love.

The more you let your negativity eat at you, the more you are losing control, losing confidence, and allowing your self-esteem to hit an all time low. It's time to stand tall and take revenge on your own mind. Fight back, because it's worth the fight, and you're worth that fight. Show up and show yourself how strong you are - even when no one is looking.

Take matters in your own hands and get revenge on that negative mindset. Fueling your thoughts with love, compassion, and forgiveness, is the only way to bust out of negative and ugly thinking. When you start practicing this over and over again, your mind will transform into a positive place! You will gain back what you lost.

I want you to use this hashtag as a reminder of who you are and Whose you are, because God made you beautiful, capable, and special. You are unlike anyone else.

Use #revengemind on your social media channels, and tag me so I can pray for you!

Consider this to be like a workout. It needs to be done daily and consistently to get a stronger mind and a stronger self esteem; it's just like people workout consistently to get stronger bodies!

When you have a fitness goal to lose weight or to lift heavier, you must exercise those muscles on a regular basis. We can't forget to exercise our minds daily, and we have to stop letting negative thinking derail us from the path God wants us to be on.

Are you ready to take on a new revenge mind with me? With all the chaos going on in the world around us, it's time to take charge and end those nasty thoughts. You are the only one who can really make a difference in your own life. Unfortunately, the longer you let negativity breed in your mind, the harder it will be to transition out of it.

God sees your pain and heartache, and He wants to take it from you. But if you keep holding on to the negative thoughts that divide you and Him, it will be harder for you to see His work in your life. Let #revengemind be the fuel to fire you up in a new and positive way!

Lord Jesus, only You and I know my thoughts. I am asking You to help me take on a revenge mind every single time negative thinking enters, or when I start feeling discouraged in any way. I will not allow the devil to steal my joy and peace anymore.

Faith is the confident assurance that what we hope for is going to happen. It is the evidence of things we cannot see.

- Hebrews 11:1

Little Tony

When I found out I was pregnant with a son I was beyond ecstatic, especially since I already had my angelic daughter, Taylor. It was my dream to have a son and a daughter, so God was so good! When Tony was born, he was perfect, and I was in love, as all mothers feel about their children.

When he turned 6 months old, something went wrong. He started vomiting out of the blue without any sick symptoms. He was an extremely happy baby, but when I took him to the park or just outside, he would get sick. I knew this was not right but the doctors kept telling me he was ok.

After a few weeks of this, we woke up one day and Tony's eyes were crossed. My husband and I immediately brought him to the eye doctor. The doctor looked at us with major concern, and he told us Tony may have a brain tumor. We had to get to the ER now!

As my body was shaking, I found strength inside me that I didn't know I had. We sat in the ER waiting patiently to hear our baby would be ok. As we found out it wasn't a brain tumor, we also found out that the fluid that travels from the stomach to the head wasn't circulating correctly, and was causing build up in his head. At this time, we knew he had an unusually large head, but assumed it was normal.

Over the next few weeks little baby Tony was getting numerous spinal taps to drain this fluid, because it kept building up. The doctors then told us that in order to get the fluid under control, he would need a shunt system put in his head right away. Otherwise, he could get brain damage.

I sat in prayer, as I was distressed day after day over a 4 week period. One of my very best friends called me, and told me to get him immediately to Boston Children's Hospital. That is exactly what we did.

I was grasping for answers, but not getting anywhere with our current hospital. They immediately took him in and set up surgery to place a shunt in his head the next morning.

As I sat in the waiting room drained from sleeping at the hospital for weeks, a young boy around 18 years old sat next to me. He asked why I was there, and I began to explain. I sat in fear, and I felt so anxious.

But then this young boy began to tell me that his best friend who was 19 years old had a shunt his whole life, and he was thriving as an all American athlete!
I sat in awe of his story, and immediately, a weight lifted off my shoulders.

He appeared in my weakest moment, and I never saw that boy again. However, I knew God placed him next to me that day, because my whole mindset shifted in an instant from fear to faith.

Tony is now 15 years old and thriving in life. He is our little miracle and I know God has big plans for him. I never give up praying for a complete healing over him, but I know he is completely in God's hands.

When fear tries to grip you or take over your mind, this is your reminder to pray. God knows your outcome; worry and fear do not have a place in those moments.

Relying on God and praying your heart out is the only way to help you get through any and all tough situations where your human strength is weak. He is strong.

Prayer

Lord, even in the midst of my troubles right now, I am relying on Your strength to get me through. I am releasing the outcome, the fear, the worry, and giving it all to You so You can equip and empower me right now to get through this day.

Then Jesus said, "come to me, all of you who are weary and carry heavy burdens, and I will give you REST. Take my yoke upon you, let me teach you, because I am humble and gentle, and you will find REST for your souls."

[Emphasis added.]

- Matthew 11:28-29

Success Lives in REST

R-E-S-T: RELEASE EVERY SINGLE THING.

When you think of the word rest, I can probably guess that you are not thinking of moments during your days. Maybe rest means finally finishing your work day and crashing on the couch, or getting into bed at night and calling it a day. My question is, where and when do you find rest in your days? Do you ever even think about it? Or, do you wake up and immediately start running a race for the next 12-15 hours? Do you find yourself spinning out of control at times with too much on your plate?

Running from one thing to another and being in a constant state of motion has never done any good for me personally. There was a time when I thought being so busy and cramming my schedule was making me feel successful, but in the end I was tired, exhausted, depressed, and lonely. "Why am I doing this to myself?" I would think. More money? More success?

I remember being so busy that I was cutting out time with those I loved the most. I put my precious family on the back burner. I was making my "busyness" an idol, and it was spinning me out of control.

I was chasing being busy, because I thought it equaled success. When I look back, I lost all that time and cannot get it back. My kids and my husband would watch me sit in my office at night after dinner on my computer while they were all snuggled on the couch watching a show. Man, I wish I could go back in time and do that part over again. But of course, that's not happening.

What IS happening though, is that I have changed everything. I've decided to REST and Release Every Single Thing to God.

Running around all day, especially in my head, gave me headaches because I was constantly searching for more. There was no rest to be found. Whether it was to fill my time with friends, continuously creating new programs, emails, or whatever else that could keep me busy, all led to fatigue mentally and physically. But again, I considered this to be "success" in my mind.

Thinking that being busy equaled being successful was so far from the truth.

I woke up one morning, exhausted, and I realized I needed actual REST. I began to ask God to calm me down and create a new path for me. I was tired of doing things the same way and getting the same results. I needed to find rest and have a clearer picture of my goals and what needs to get done in one single day.

My answers were always found by opening the Bible and reading the Word. When I fuel my mind with Godly advice or reading a chapter, it is like He awakens my spirit and brings calmness to my soul.

If you are tired of running around in your mind, and you feel exhausted about your days, give yourself a few moments to completely rest in God. Let Him fuel you up with His advice, His love, and His peace so you can take your next steps with confidence. Even as a Christian, I need to be reminded of this constantly because I can get caught up in life. When I put Jesus on the back burner, everything becomes more messy.

Life doesn't have to be as chaotic as we think, and God is waiting for those special moments to spend with you alone. He can fill your gas tank with exactly what it needs in the exact moment it needs. If you are looking to be more successful in your life, try resting more with God and watch what will unfold for you. He has big plans for you, and He wants you to be successful! Just trust Him, and have faith that He is always in control.

God will always make a way when there seems to be no way.

Prayer

Heavenly Father, I am coming to You to find rest, and I am releasing all my thoughts and anxious feelings to You right now. Make a new way and a new path for me to follow. Renew my faith and my mind to trust You along the way.

For I am about to do a brand new thing. See, I have already begun! Do you not see it? I will make a pathway through the wilderness for my people to come home. I will create rivers for them in the desert.

- Isaiah 43:19

✝ *Fuel*

A New Revival Is On The Way

The word revival means to take something that was once dead and bring it to life. This is exactly what God wants to do in our lives. You will have moments where things come to an end, or you lose hope. When that happens, read Isaiah 43:19 again, and trust that God is ready to revive something in your life.

After leading Kelley's Bootcamp for 10 years, new owners came in and bought the gym where I rented space. In a quick moment, they closed the doors on me and my business. Through my coaching, training, and leading hundreds of women to physical and mental transformations, I felt like everything I worked for died that day. Not only did I just lose my mother a few short months before this, I also lost my business. My insides felt crushed and dead.

How can this have happened to me? What was I supposed to do now? As I was feeling worthless and having that pity party that we all tend to have from time to time, I remembered God saying that He would do a new thing. I had to firmly put my trust in Him, and I waited. As months started to pass, I felt a revival in my spirit telling me there's more for me to accomplish. "It's not over Kelley," God said, and this got me excited. This was the exact fuel I needed to bring life back into me.

Do you ever find yourself actually staying in the pity party too long? Sometimes it can get a little too comfortable, and that is exactly what I was doing. When you go through a loss of some kind, it can knock the wind out of you. Letting yourself feel your feelings is ok, but staying in those sad feelings will only cause a snowball effect. The more you let yourself stay there, the harder it will be to get out. I knew I didn't want to stay in that place!

When you find yourself at the end of the road, or you feel hopeless, lost and possibly dead inside, I want you to remember that God is there to awaken your spirit if you will let Him.

I began to pray and ask Him what my next steps could be, because I truly didn't know how to transition next. Each day as I prayed, I woke up to the fact that God created each one of us on purpose and for a purpose. I wrote down those words so they would be fresh in my mind every single day. I want you to fully believe this too.

What happened next was that my podcast launched! I named it Addicted To The Climb. God will always make a way, especially when there seems to be no way if you let Him. He wants to do a brand new thing for you. He will create a new pathway, even through the wilderness. Trust Him, let Him, and open your heart for a new beginning. God will always make a way when there seems to be no way. Let us always remind ourselves of that.

If you are in need of a revival in your life, ask God to wake you up in a new area. After all, His desire for you is to see you thrive not just survive.

Lord, fuel me up and awaken my spirit to something new and fresh. I am ready to let You lead the way, and even if there are moments of uncertainty, I will put my trust in You.

Trust in Him at all times, you people; pour out your hearts to Him, for God is our refuge.

– Psalm 62:8

Miracles Can Happen When You Believe

I want to tell you about Paul "Cooch" O'Mara, my dad.

One day in the fall of 2016, my parents got a phone call that their best friend had a heart attack and was in the hospital.

I remember running up to that hospital with them, since he was like family. I sat with his 23 year old daughter, who had just lost her mother 18 months before. We spent almost a week there with the family while he was in the ICU.

One night, as I was driving home with my parents, my dad explained that he just got diagnosed with a rare blood cancer. We needed to set up some appointments to talk about treatment.

Picture my head spinning in circles, because as far back as I can remember as a child, my dad was probably the healthiest person I knew. I don't think he ever took an aspirin in his life. He didn't have great eating habits overall, but he was an avid runner who took care of his body physically, running 5-8 miles a day.

So to hear the words that he had a rare cancer was a shock for my mother and I. As we sat with teams of doctors and learned from a few of them that his chances were not that great, we headed to Boston's Dana Farber.

Those doctors gave us hope and encouraged us that my dad will be ok, and that he was in great hands. He needed to undergo a stem cell transplant, and we immediately got on a donor list.

In April 2017, he got the call that there was a donor in Germany with the same blood type as him, so we were ready to go and start the process and treatment. They told us he would be in the hospital for at least one month, so my mother and I buckled up for the journey together.

Even though my mother was not healthy due to rheumatoid arthritis, she still showed up every single day (full face of makeup and looking beautiful) to go with me to visit my father.

He had intense chemo for a whole week, he lost all his hair and it wiped out his whole immune system. I never saw my father so weak and fragile. The next week was his stem cell transplant. This was the scariest moment of our lives, and fear had started to grip us.

My father had been my mother's caregiver for 40 years and to see him like this and not know if he would survive it, was overwhelming to say the least. Silent tears would trickle down my mother's face, and I knew I had to be strong for her. We kept praying and leaving it in God's hands, because we were so weak. We pulled from His strength at all times.

One day while dad was sleeping, my mother stood over his bed and prayed a prayer I'll never forget. She said,

"Lord Jesus, only you know the outcome of this procedure, and I know you are going to heal this man so he can be the talk of the hospital. You are going to make this man a miracle for the doctors to see, and he is going to have a full recovery. Thank You, Jesus, for Your healing hands and shining your light on him right now. In Jesus' name we pray."

I was balling my eyes out. Yet, my mother and I had such peace that day. Three weeks passed by, and the doctors said my father's blood counts were incredible. He could go home 1 week early!

We were not surprised, because we knew the hand of God was in this. Like my mother said, he was a complete miracle. Even though he was still so sick when he came home and had to be in isolation for one year, we knew he would be OK.

Unfortunately 3 weeks after that, as we were all home and handling his recovery, my mother suddenly passed of an aneurysm.

My prayer for you right now is to stay close to God no matter what happens in your life. You will want to give up and quit, but please don't! Ask God right now to continually help you in your thoughts so you never give up on Him.

He loves you and wants the best for you, but life is full of setbacks. You need to buckle up and grab hold of God's hand as you journey through life. He will never leave you nor forsake you. Without hope and faith, people perish.

Lord, I want to feel Your healing hands in my life. I believe that You are in control of all things and you already know the outcome of everything in my life. Help me hang on to Your loving promises so I never waiver in my faith. Thank You, Jesus, for hearing my prayers.

✝ Fuel

You are what you eat, and the food you choose, is your mood.

- Kelley Tyan

You Are What You Eat

Do you remember that commercial from the 80's that says, "you are what you eat, and you are what you swallow, so remember that next time you feel hollow?' You can watch it on YouTube because the words and the meaning are still significant today. (Look up Time For Timer: "You Are What You Eat PSA" 1983)

Every time you eat, you may notice that you feel a certain way. It might be satisfied, calm, proud, bloated, still hungry, or too full. Whatever it is, I want you to start paying close attention to this detail. Food is your fuel, just as gasoline is the fuel to run your car.

Your God-created body was not made to eat processed foods with artificial ingredients because these things slow you down. They can cause other negative side effects that I know you would rather not have.

How have you fueled your body today? Or this week so far? Is it from God made foods that make you feel incredible, or are you giving into temptations with processed foods that are leading you down a negative road? When you ignore the side effects, you are ignoring the root cause of why you are eating the things you choose.

At the end of the day, what you eat gives you feelings of satisfaction or dissatisfaction. When I am coaching my clients, the most common phrase I hear is, "I feel so guilty and bad about what I ate yesterday.' Is this how you want to live your life? I truly don't believe that to be true.

Today is your new chance to start fresh and make a positive change. Incorporate one small decision today. That could be adding in a fruit instead of a sugary snack, or adding in more vegetables on your plate to keep you full longer. One small step in the right direction can lead to big success by the end of the week.

What changes can you start today to feel better in your body? What is one food you can replace with a God made choice?

If you ever find yourself running in circles all day chasing coffee drinks or sugar, it's time to wake up to the fact that these habits are leading you down a road of weight gain, exhaustion, or even shameful thinking. I have personally been in those situations, and I know what it feels like to want to make a change so badly.

I also knew that I needed help and couldn't make the changes I wanted alone. One thing I did realize is that when my gas tank is low or running on junk, my mind is not at peace. I bet you can relate to this in some way, and maybe you know exactly how I have felt. Learning to stop my own chaos from escalating even more and leaning into God to find rest and peace is the only way I would come back stronger.

Taking a time out and asking God to help you see more clearly will give you the courage to take strategic action. I know food can be a struggle at times, but I also know and realize that we all have the same exact choices at the end of the day. Growing up as a junk foodie and remembering all the stomach issues and migraines I suffered with, as well as low self esteem and body issues, taught me that I never want to feel that way again.

I know if I can constantly make better choices that will fuel my body the way God wants me to, so can you! We are no different; you just have to dig deep and decide what is most important to you, your health, or your feelings in the moments of temptation.

Prayer

Lord, I want to fuel my body with good nutrition so I can live a full and active life. Help me to overcome temptation and give me the courage to choose the foods I know will be best for my body.

Feel the fear, and do it anyway.

- Kelley Tyan

Fear Is A Choice

When you first start something new, it can be extremely scary. You might not know what you are doing yet, but you keep going, right?

This is how I felt when I thought about creating my podcast. My mind lit up with the words Addicted To The Climb, and that was definitely a download from God himself. I knew I had a message to get out to the world and to help people stay on the climb of life without giving up, so the podcast was born. When my friend Heather came to visit me, as she always did during Thanksgiving, she told me to sit down right then and there and press record to interview her.

Even though she was one of my closest friends, I froze and fear was written all over my face. But I knew if I didn't just start, I would stay frozen in that fear. Who wants to stay living in that way? Not me, and not you.

When you have a great idea, or a thought that it's time to take action, the only way to find out if you made the right decision is to jump right in and push the fear out the door. If you don't do this, it will fester and keep you stuck.

Have you wanted to start a new clean eating plan so badly but you kept putting it off and the weight kept creeping up? Maybe you were fearful that you wouldn't stick to it, and then you would disappoint yourself. So instead of trying, you gave in to those negative thoughts telling you to wait.

Or, you have been single for too long but scared to take a leap and go on a date! What about telling yourself that you are waiting for the "right time" to start that thing, but that "right time" never came. If this is you, it's time to make a decision and put yourself first on your list today. I know you have a to-do list, and I know your name is not on it!

These examples are all significant and real for many people. However, God created us NOT to be fearful and wants us to be successful in what we do. When it comes down to it, fear is a choice, and I believe God will never give us more than we can handle. If you are frozen with fear over something you know needs to be done, or started, it's time to pray boldly and ask God to give you His supernatural strength to take a firm stand towards it.

Having a morning prayer routine has changed the way I think, and now I have learned that when I pray about something unknown, I trust that God is leading the way. Try trading in your fears for God's strength and watch how much you will grow from there. Even if the thing doesn't end the way you thought it would, at least you can say you tried. That is a win and that is the fuel you need to do it again.

Lord, I am trading in all my fears for Your strength and mighty power that will allow me to move forward and keep on climbing to new heights. I know You are with me on this journey, and no matter what the end result is, we are in it together.

What if….everything you are going through is preparing you for what you asked for?

- Kelley Tyan

I Once Was Blind, But Now I See

Sitting in your own misery is not a good place to be. When you're in that place, it's just you, all alone, focusing on all your problems.

Sometimes, the heaviness can get hard to bear. I did this often, and it took a toll on my health. I would dwell on negative thoughts about why my mother had to die...Why did I have to get breast cancer...Why did my healthy dad who never even had a cold, get diagnosed with a rare blood cancer...Why was my son born with hydrocephalus? Why? Why? Why?

Sitting around crying about what happened to me through these circumstances not only was making me weak, but I was also becoming unattached to the people around me. Looking back on this time, I see that I was slowly unraveling.

In the back of my head, I knew I should draw closer to God, but I wanted to resist. Because I didn't want to feel better; I wanted to cry. I would tell myself that I deserved these things to happen to me, because why should I be exempt?

One night, in the midst of this chaos, God actually shook me up and woke me up to His presence and His answers.

I knew He was there and loved me so much that He didn't want me to stay this way. (Nor does He want you to either, if you relate to this story.)

As I began to pray, I asked Him to take this burden off me and show me how to strengthen my faith again. Subconsciously, I didn't want to feel this tremendous sadness, and I desperately wanted to feel better. I had felt my faith was fading, and I knew I had to address the issue before it was too late.

The mind is a funny and torturous thing. One minute it says, "You are desperate, you are unworthy," and the next, "You have confidence, and you feel strong." That's the devil for you: He's always trying to get you to believe the lies that he sneaks in your head.

I was being blinded by sadness, guilt, and turmoil. It was trying to knock me right back down to when I was in the middle of those situations, even though they were over. They were in the past, and I had to become present. I had a choice. We all have a choice in these moments, and you can never forget that.

As I prayed each day and read my Bible, God immediately showed me scriptures that repaired my heart, mind, and soul. My focus was rearranged, and little by little, He showed me all the beautiful things that I do have. He showed me to focus on those, instead of focusing on what I had lost. Psalm 32:7 was one of those verses, and it says, "You are my hiding place; you will protect me from trouble and surround me with songs of deliverance." That verse does NOT say, "You will be protected from any and all trouble." It tells us that, even though there IS trouble in your midst, God will deliver you from it! He is your hiding place. I hung onto that verse every time unhealthy thoughts entered my mind, and I always felt peace instead of anger. My heart was melting, and love was entering back in.

Here were some of my new thoughts: I have a healthy and thriving son who plays sports, and I am so proud of the man he is becoming. I have a beautiful and blessed marriage. My mother is with her Savior, Jesus. I am a survivor. My precious daughter and I are thriving in our relationship right now. My dad is completely healed and living an amazing life at this moment.

Sometimes we focus so much on what we lost and what we don't have instead of seeing what we do have. As my eyes became opened to what God showed me, my life took a complete turn. This is exactly what I want for you right now.

If you are going through a challenging time or feeling lost, anxious or unhappy, there is some inner work that needs to be done. God will show up if you ask Him to. He wants to meet you right where you are: broken, most, and afraid. That is the God we serve, and if you lean in to Him, He will lean in harder to you. If you feel anger or distressed by what you lost, let God repair your mind and help you so you can recover and move forward.

Life is always going to be full of hurdles, loss, grief, and sorrow. However, God is greater than all of our worries and fears. He can and is ready to restore your mind and soul. There is always a bigger and better plan that God has for us, but sometimes He only allows us to see bits and pieces of it until we are ready. Instead of asking why something happened to you, open up your heart and let

Him fill you up with His purpose and His promises of your life.

Dwelling on your negative circumstances will only breed more negativity. Believe me: I did that for way too long, and it only kept me hostage to those feelings. It's time to turn doubt into determination so you can live at peace, and you can have hope and courage to move forward.

Prayer

Lord, open up my eyes so I can see Your loving presence through my circumstances. No matter what I am facing, I believe and trust that You will make a way and help me see Your goodness through it all.

Yet to all who did receive Him, to those who believed in HIs name, He gave the right to become children of God.

- John 1:12

Identity: Who Are You?

Repeat after me: I am a child of God.

Do you realize that God sees your life, and it is significant to Him?

I used to play small in certain areas of my life. I would pretend I didn't matter or my work here didn't matter. I also thought no one cared, because why would they?

There were times I set myself back because I thought I didn't have what it took, like the other women I was watching succeed. Why do we do this to ourselves? How silly is that to think? Have you ever felt that way before?

What if your daughter, niece, or grandchild said something like that to you? How would you respond? Would you tell him or her that you agree, or to just stay put and not try, or would you say to keep trying anyways?

I want you to know that God sees you as His child, and you are significant to Him in every single way. He made no mistakes, and no matter what you are going through or have been through, or even what you are building right now, He is right there by your side. You are significant, and your life is to Him who created you.

I sat with my son one day and explained this. I realized that at 15 years old, children are being chased down and attacked by social media, TV shows, and sometimes friends, who tell them what they are supposed to act like, think like, and BE like.

Without knowing that your identity is in Christ alone, a person can really start believing the lies being told.

I explained to him that only God's thoughts mattered, and to always trust his gut. I told him that this is way more important than relying on other people's thoughts and opinions of you. You will never be enough to someone else, but in God, you are fully complete, worthy, and beautiful. Knowing and believing that you are a child of God is freeing, and bondage from thinking otherwise can be broken.

Are you playing small right now because you think no one cares or sees you? God sees you! He wants you to start shining your light inside your community, inside your family, and inside your circle of friends. Your life is meaningful and has a purpose.

Today, I want you to fuel up on knowing and realizing that YOU were made for more. Wherever you are right now is not where God wants you to stay. Without challenge, there is no growth. Without change, you will stay stagnant.

Are you comfortable where you are right now? Happy? Fulfilled?

If you are stuck in a rut, I want you to refuse to accept things the way they are. Instead, make a small change to start your new climb with God by your side.

Since I started taking Him with me everywhere I go, life has a whole different meaning. Coming from trying to find who I was and what my identity was, now I know it was inside me the whole time. Just like your identity is in you.

You are not living to please other people, and you don't have to prove to anyone that you have what it takes. God already knows you have what it takes! Now, He wants you to start showing up as him or her.

What is the dream you have always had, but felt you felt too insignificant to follow it through? Write out your thoughts and a new game plan so you can start taking action and feel significant as God feels about you.

As long as you are living and breathing, you can achieve your goals and fulfill your purpose. Your identity is in Christ alone, and He is waiting to show you the way.

Prayer

Lord, thank You for creating me perfectly in your image. Thank You that I do not have to prove myself anymore because it is exhausting. Thank You for helping me realize my significance here on Earth, and I am excited to live my purpose and fulfill my dreams with You by my side.

The joy is in the journey.

– John Bingham

Release The Outcome

When you start showing up in an area that you want to improve, you must not focus on the outcome each day. Instead, do the work and release the outcome to God.

I remember when I first started working out and getting more serious about weight lifting. I wanted to see changes in my body overnight. I would be shocked that in 1 week (Mon-Friday to be exact), my abs weren't showing!

We all live in a microwave society, but sadly our bodies take more time than a few days to get lean. Just like our bodies, it takes more than a week for changes in any area of our lives to start happening.

I realized right away that I had to stop focusing on the future and how long the process was going to take for me to achieve my goal.

I had to release the outcome and just keep showing up no matter what I was going through or even if I didn't notice any changes.

Most people quit right before the magic happens because they want to see changes as fast as they start. Teaching clients to release the outcome has been transformational in my coaching. By doing this, it takes the pressure off, and it gives the power back to the person on the journey.

Think about a time when you were working on a health goal, and you lost some weight. Wasn't it exciting throughout the process as you tried clothes on that were once too tight, and then they fit better? I bet you had a pep in your step that day! Maybe you even continued doing what you know would give you even more results.

Learning how to enjoy the journey, even through the challenges it may come with, will bring you more joy than you can ever imagine, as long as you change your mind-set about the results.

Sometimes, it is not the actual results that make us stronger, it's the actual journey that transforms us in mind and soul.

When you release the outcome and the stress about the end goal, you will start to realize that your focus is on the day to day work you put in. Ask yourself what you can do better than you did the week before?

If you have a dream, a goal, or a new climb that is scary right now, that means it's time to focus, take messy action, and start the journey. It is not going to be easy, but you are capable. Leave the stress, the worry, and the fears all to God, because His strength is definitely far more greater than our own.

Your job is to stay consistent with your plan, lay your excuses outside your door, and don't even think of giving up. Since you are reading this right now, God has placed something on your heart. He wants to take every little step with you to get you to the top of that mountain. Are you ready to show up differently this time?

Releasing the outcome is your new way of conquering what you have always wanted to achieve and now is your time, no more waiting or watching someone else.

Prayer

Heavenly Father, I am giving up control of the outcome right now. Help me to enjoy the journey, no matter what I face. Give me the strength to keep on climbing and the mentality to be strong enough to finish what I start.

If It Is To Be, It's Up To Me!

- William Johnson

Learning How To Unlearn Old Habits

At my very first network marketing conference over 20 years ago, one of my mentors said this saying on stage: "If it is to be, then it is up to me." That woman was on stage with diamonds dripping from her ears and neck with so many awards in her hands. She earned them all herself from the company. Nothing was handed to her. She earned every little piece of her success.

I was sitting in the audience in awe of her. Not only was she impacting many people's lives through her business, but she also forged her own way, and created a path of success for herself.

Now, over 20 years later, I am still part of a company similar to that, because I still love the thought of being in control of my own success and how high I want to climb. Having this control continues to teach me to be sure God is always my CEO directing my steps.

I have realized that the more I fuel my mind with positive thoughts, and if I keep working hard, accomplishment and success will happen. I also realized that if I quit or give up, nothing will ever happen.

Everything you have learned over the years has a huge impact on how you approach your life, your business, your faith, and your health. Sometimes, what we have learned is not always benefiting us in the best way possible.

For example, 10 years ago when I was competing in fitness, I had learned that I had to eat 6 meals a day. This is what the fitness experts were writing in all the magazines, and teaching. That eating style worked out for me in the end. However, when it came to coaching my clients in the same way, they were not getting the same results I did.

When you realize what you have been doing is not working anymore, there has to be a change that takes place. I call it, "unlearning what you have learned," and this is a very hard thing for many people.

Have you ever kept doing the same thing over and over and felt frustrated that you were not getting results? If you want to see change, you have to change and it is only up to you to start the new process.

If you have formed unhealthy habits that are constantly dragging you down, it's time to learn and practice new ones.

Whether you are in business for yourself and climbing the success ladder, or you are working towards better health and weight loss, nothing will happen until you decide to make it happen.

If it is to be, it's up to you to keep on climbing. Keep the recording playing continuously in your head with positive affirmations that you can and will accomplish what you started. No one ever remembers the person who gave up, but they will remember the ones who didn't.

Be the one. Make yourself proud, even if no one is looking.

Prayer

Lord, thank You for giving me so many opportunities to succeed in life. You are in control of the outcome, and I am willing to take the steps necessary to stay on the climb ahead of me. Please give me strength to defeat my negative thoughts. and help me form new and better habits that will give me peace.

You have the power to say, "This is not how my story will end."

- Christine Mason Miller

Hold Your Pen To Write Your Story

What legacy will you leave behind?
Of courage?
Of strength?
Of never giving up on yourself?
Of paving your own path?
Of being a leader?

This is your time! Right at this very moment, I want you to grab a pen and start writing out your brand new story. Yesterday is gone, and tomorrow may never come, but today is here for you to start over. Start something new today that will make you feel proud. Include Jesus, Who is always by your side, cheering you on when no one else is watching.

Make a promise to yourself that you will write one sentence every single day that will get you excited enough to propel you up the stairs that are very steep ahead.

After my mother passed, I was left all alone in my own thoughts while I was grieving. The grief was so strong and I remember thinking I wouldn't be able to smile ever again. I also remember thinking that I would never be strong enough to lead or empower women again, as I did before she passed.

Then the moment came where I had a choice to put the pen back in my own hand or just hide in my grief and sadness. I decided to grab the pen and start writing.

That very small action step gave me the courage that I needed. It helped me see myself the way God saw me: beautiful, courageous, and strong. Every morning when I woke up, it was challenging emotionally and mentally, but I knew God would make a way. I know He wants to make a way for you.

The more I begin to pray and fuel my mind with God's word, the more it becomes alive inside me. Even though I am still writing my story continuously, I know from now on I will never put my pen down no matter what happens in my life.

Make a brand new promise to yourself right now that you'll start writing your beautiful story today. You were manufactured by God Himself, and all the God given qualities you possess are already inside you.

Think about a time when you felt the most loved. What about a proud moment in your life? I bet you can list many of these moments, and they will pile up.

All of these are part of your story. Every day you have a chance to create new memories, and although the road isn't going to be smooth the entire way, you will get through it with God.

Take charge and take action to live a faith-filled life with trust that your Father in Heaven is always making a way for you.

The question to constantly ask yourself is, "What is it costing me to stay in the same place?" If it is costing you frustration, agony, or feeling stagnant, only you know exactly what has to be done. God will lead you and open doors for you, but only if you get up and make a move.

Prayer

Father, I want to write my story with You by my side, opening up new doors for me to grow and become the best version of myself. Even in my low moments, I will trust that You already know the ending to my story and will keep me on Your path. Thank You for letting me wake up each morning with a renewed mind to start over.

Fitness

Beautifully and Wonderfully Made

Introduction

You made all the delicate, inner parts of my body and knit me together in my mother's womb. Thank you for making me so wonderfully complex.
- Psalm 139: 13-15

The meaning of the word fitness has really evolved over the years, especially since my early 20's. Back then, it was all about physical results, vanity, and working out to prove something. It was mostly for other people, and it was exhausting especially in my mind. I was focusing on all the wrong things, such as too much cardio to be skinny, not enough food, comparing myself constantly, and trying to achieve unrealistic body goals for myself.

It wasn't until my mid thirties that I finally realized that being fit was more of a mindset than an action. It didn't have to be a struggle or a chore. It could actually be fun and exciting.

What significantly changed was the way I looked at my workouts and my own body. I finally started to accept that my body was a true gift from God. He made me unique; unlike anyone else. This goes for you too. This new thinking started to sink in more and more, and I began to believe it. The more I told myself God loves me just as I am and that I get to workout, instead of I need to workout, my outlook on fitness became extremely fun and rewarding.

Of course, I always want to look my best, however, the way I think about fitness is all about being healthy from the inside out, so I can accomplish more in my life.

My old thoughts about chasing an unrealistic body led me down tortuous paths of self-destruction and unhealthy habits. I remember there were times when I would stand in front of my mirror and cry. I held onto those demons and nasty thoughts for years, and I want to save you from the torment so you can love the skin you're in. That way, you can always take care of it with good intentions.

My thoughts were always telling me I needed to work harder, skip meals, starve myself, and so on. Can you relate to this in any way too? Do you suffer from having a strong negative self talk trying to keep you from living your happiest and healthiest life?

I finally turned to God because I couldn't live like that anymore. He showed me who I was, and that I was His perfect child. Do you know that YOU are perfect just the way you are? Yes, God wants you to live a healthy life and always keep your body moving, but He also does not want you living in shame or tearing yourself apart.

I can now say that I am addicted to fitness, because moving my body lights me up in ways I never experienced before. I throw on a great podcast, and I lean on God to continue helping me get strong physically and mentally. When you workout for God, your mind gets strengthened in so many ways too! What started as a chore, is now a beautiful lifestyle. Whether your fitness is taking long walks or going to the gym, do it all for the glory of God and try seeing yourself the way He does: Beautiful and wonderfully made.

This section is all about YOU! Even if you are overweight, feeling unmotivated, or suffer from low confidence, I have walked in your shoes! Today is going to be the day you decide to change everything. All it takes is one thought that leads to one decision, that leads to creating new habits that will stick. Are you ready?

If you don't like something,
change it. If you can't change it,
change the way you think about it.

- Maya Angelou

Your Strongest Muscle

Do you realize that your mind is the strongest muscle in your body? Your body can be extremely fit, but if your mind is not, you will never feel fit, fulfilled, or enough. You have complete control over how powerful it is, so why aren't you relying on God's promises?

I am guilty of this too at times. But at some point in your lives, within your goals and desires, you must stop and make the changes that will push you along further, instead of holding you back.

I obviously despise the fact that I had cancer. I used to pretend that it didn't happen because I would feel completely depressed. I never talked about it with ANYONE, not even my family. The real reason why is because I didn't want to face the truth of it, and that was torturing me inside.

As I was doing this, it was building up inside and would bring me to tears when I was alone. I hated feeling that way all the time, but one day I realized that my outlook about it was all wrong. Instead of trying to avoid thinking about it all together, which was hard to do, I faced it head on and rearranged my thoughts about it.

I decided to speak of my healing and give God the glory to help others that needed hope too. I told myself that

I wasn't a survivor anymore, I am now thriving in my life and I will never give up on myself.

Changing the way I looked at my diagnosis created a whole new mindset. It took away all the pain I connected to it. I once felt ashamed, sad, and guilty that I didn't do something right in my life. I had to transform my thinking and create a new sound mind around it so I could start living my life to the fullest again, without despair and depression.

I now want to get on the rooftops and tell everyone I had cancer! I know it will bring people hope that if I could overcome this, they can too. When your mind starts to play tricks on you, as mine did, let God help you realize that His plans are far greater than yours. He wants you to thrive in life so you can tell your own story of being an overcomer.

Fitness is not just about transforming your body, it is also about transforming your thoughts towards yourself and around the circumstances you will face. Exercising your mind starts with taking baby steps just as working out does. You might not wake up everyday feeling happy or excited about life, especially if you are going through something with your health. But with God's help, He can change the way you think about things.

Having cancer was a humbling experience that made me rethink just about everything in my life. No one is exempt from heartache, death, or even disease, but life can be so much better when you surrender your thoughts to God. It all starts by asking Him to renew your mind each morning when you wake up.

I am urging you to keep feeding your faith, not the fears that try to cripple you. If you agree with me and believe this to be true, then you need to start exercising your mind every day the same way you need to exercise your body. Bible reading, journaling, and sitting quietly praying is how I start the day. How do you start yours?

Prayer

Lord Jesus, please help me focus my thoughts on You, especially when I feel fear or hopelessness. Whatever I am facing, I know You are with me, and I want to use my story of being an overcomer to lift others up.

Motivation is what gets you started; habit is what keeps you going.

— Jim Ryun

Do You Really Feel Like It?

Are you only motivated when you feel good? Or when things are going your way?

I'll be honest; that is NOT the way getting healthy and fit works. If I only got up when I felt good, or only moved my body because I was in a good mood, that would only be 1/2 my life! LOL.

I am human like you. In fact, I have suffered from horrible menstrual cycles since I was 12 years old, month after month. There are days when I am in so much pain that I don't want to get out of bed.

However, I realized that if on those days I stay laying in bed, I am feeding into my pain, and letting it take me over, instead of me taking it over! I show up and get up to move my body even when I am tired and not feeling like it. This is because at the end of the day, I know I will feel proud. I am no different from you. I don't possess any superpowers that you don't have.

Here is where your mind has to go: your motivation has to come from deep within, and you have to tell yourself that no matter what happens in your life, you will keep going. This is a promise I have to myself many years ago now.

It doesn't happen overnight. However, if you keep reminding yourself of your promise, it will be harder to let yourself down every day. The only person that can motivate you is yourself. When you keep doing the same thing over and over it will become a habit, just like waking up and brushing your teeth. If you keep allowing yourself off the hook from exercising or eating clean, that also becomes a habit.

I challenge you today to keep your promise to yourself of how you will get healthier. Are you needing to drink more water? Get to a workout class? Go for a walk? No matter what it is, keep doing what truly makes you happy, even when you don't feel like it.

Talk with God about your new plan, and get excited to start showing up differently than how you used to. What new promise will you make to yourself today? How are you going to motivate yourself differently this time?

God made your body to move, and it is a sacred temple! So treat it that way.

Thank You, Father, for giving me strength to follow through with my promise to myself. Help me keep pushing myself even when I don't feel like it. Give me the motivation and the want to get healthier for myself and You.

_____

_____

_____

_____

_____

_____

_____

_____

_____

_____

If it doesn't challenge you, it won't change you.

- Fred DeVito

Comfort Zones Are Boring

Who doesn't love staying inside their cozy comfort zone? I know I do at times. You stay put right where you are because it is routine. After all, you don't want to ruffle any feathers, especially your own.

When I find life getting monotonous and a little boring, I look at the routine I am in right away. Am I just walking through my days doing the same thing over and over, or am I tapping into others for motivation or a new challenge?

Don't get me wrong, I LOVE being in my comfort zone at times. However, when I step out of it and try something new, there is a new fire inside me that I seem to forget to light. When I remember, I come alive in a different way.

Being an entrepreneur means you work alone. That is exactly what I have been doing most of my life: Working alone. It can get lonely at times, and for many years, I just assumed it is what it is. Then I figured out there are numerous groups of women in masterminds working together to level up together. As I contemplated joining one of these groups and paying for a coach, I went back and forth about it.

Honestly, I was scared to step out of my cozy place and put money into something I was extremely unsure of.

Not only was I going to be investing in this coach, but I was going to meet many other women, and I felt nervous. I had never done anything like this before, but I knew if I didn't make a move, I would most likely be in the same spot 1 year from then. I remember praying so hard for God to lead me in the way He wants me to go. I prayed before I even knew about this opportunity, and then it showed up. God wanted me to venture out and step out in faith, and that is exactly what I did.

When you pray boldly for something, then don't sleep on the fact that God shows up and answers prayer! As comfortable as I was in my life and in my business, I knew I needed change and to start growing in a new way, mentally and spiritually. The group I joined was faith-based and all about business coaching, and it was the very best decision I had made in a long time. I wished I had started doing these things earlier in my career, but I got too comfortable doing everything myself.

My point is, if you keep doing the same thing over and over again, you will get the very same results. Take this into consideration with your fitness and exercise. If you are not noticing improvements in your body, it's time to change things up even if you don't feel like it. After all, change in the body comes from challenging your muscles.

Start to trust God to help you step out of your comfort zone and into something much greater than you can imagine. Life is not supposed to be stagnant. Instead, we are supposed to evolve constantly so we can be fruitful and live out our purpose.

If you feel stuck right now and want to be renewed in mind and spirit, start praying bold prayers! Ask God to open up a new door for you.

Since that coaching I had, I have now started my podcast, wrote this book, and met the most incredible and beautiful women who are now my friends. Comfort zones are boring, so don't get stuck in one! Just remember, you are the only one who can get yourself fired up and fueled up, so make a decision today and start praying.

Prayer

Lord, I don't want to stay in the same place. I want to continually evolve into the person You created me to be. Help me see a new path or a new door that is opening for me. I am excited for great things to come in my life!

Let us not lose heart in doing good, for in due time we will reap if we do not grow weary.

- Galatians 6:9

Repetition For The Greater Good

Do you ever work out day after day or week after week and find yourself staring in the mirror focusing on that one part of your body that you think is flawed?

That's the recording I played in my head on repeat day after day, workout after workout. It was completely exhausting, and it always made me feel insecure. Repeating the negative thoughts in your head every day actually makes you believe them. Do you do that right now?

I finally woke up one day and asked God to let me see myself with His eyes, and this changed everything from that moment on. Whatever you do, do it for the Lord. Don't do it for vanity reasons, because you will never be perfect in your own eyes, no matter how hard you work out or eat clean.

You are what you repeatedly do, and you become what you repeatedly think.

When I decided to start practicing what I have been preaching, my eyes opened up to a different way of thinking. What we put on repeat in our heads, or in our routines, becomes our norm.
I wanted to start my days feeling fired up instead of feeling tired, so I picked up my Bible and dove in first thing

in the mornings. It took time for this to become a habit. The more I did it, the more alive I would feel, and my days got better and better.

As the Bible verse from Galatians says, "in due time, we will reap if we do not grow weary." Let that verse resonate with you right now, because when we do something right, we must keep on doing it and not grow weary. God will bless that thing many times over.

Another thing I do is to make sure I eat greens at least once a day, because I know my body feels it's best that way. At first, I would skip days, but now it is on repeat daily, and I have never felt better.

I have put my most important things that fuel me up on repeat. I suggest choosing only 1-2 things at first, or you will feel overwhelmed. Choose something that fires you up each day, whether it is eating 2 clean meals a day, or doing some form of movement, and put it on repeat. The more you do it, the easier it becomes, and all of a sudden, it's a brand new habit!

Today I want you to know that you are always perfect in God's eyes. He created you that way: Perfect and unique, unlike anyone else. Keep working out and taking care of what He gave you; you only have one body and one mind!

Start working out, because it is something you get to do. It empowers you to be strong in your physical body, not because it's a chore. Put that on repeat in your mind and watch what happens in your heart. You will feel more happiness, more calm, and overall better mentally.

Prayer

Heavenly Father, let me start seeing myself with Your eyes only. I want to play a love song in my head that leaves me feeling uplifted and beautiful, just the way You made me. Thank You, Lord, for giving me this body and this mind so I can accomplish big goals. Today is a new day to start a brand new recording in my mind and a new daily ritual for my body.

My health may fail, and my spirit may grow weak, but God remains the strength of my heart, He is mine forever.

– Psalm 73:26

The Power Is In Your Perspective

There have been many times when I would get on a workout streak: Day after day, week after week. I would get into my mode where I feel so incredible and treat my body like the temple God made it to be. Boom! I feel like I am on top of the world and I can conquer anything!

Then, all of a sudden, I would skip my workouts and eat things that did not make me feel good. Days would go by, sometimes weeks, and I would feel lost, upset, discouraged, and extremely disappointed in myself. It would feel almost as if I never worked out at all, because I would start to tell myself, "You lost all your momentum, and now you have to start all over...You are weak." Thus begins a vicious cycle of negative thoughts circling around in my head. Why do we do this? I know I am not alone here.

At the end of those days I would feel so bad about myself, and it would be hard to start back up. The momentum would be lost, and in the back of my mind, I always knew I had to find it again. Have you ever felt this way too? What I have realized by doing this over and over is that I lost my perspective.

A few bad days and now you think it's over. Skipping workouts for a week because you went on vacation, and now you gained all your weight back. Eating unhealthy for a few days, and now you are overweight and feeling guilty. Negative thinking creeps in, and distorted thoughts about yourself take over.

Perspective just needs a shift. I am encouraging you to see things as they are, not as failures. There are moments in life when your spirit might grow weak, but God's strength is always stronger.

Did you enjoy that week-long vacation and spend quality time with your family? Maybe you even slept in for once? Or, would you rather spend that quality time in the gym? You get to decide how to spend your time, and if it is enjoying a (not so healthy) beautiful meal with your family, it is ok! As long as you get back on track when you get home.

I have put so much pressure on myself and wasted hours of thinking I was going backwards in my health, all for nothing! All it did was waste my own time and make me feel powerless. The power lies in your own perspective of things.

Reality check: Just because you stopped working out or eating clean for a quick moment doesn't mean all your hard work is gone!

Bring your thoughts back to God, and pull from His strength not yours. Our human strength will only get us so far. It will give up, quit, and tell us we are weak.

The enemy is fighting against you at all times and wants to rob you of your joy. God wants to fill us back up, equip us with His strength to get back on our feet, and get back at it again and again.

Change your perspective and increase your faith so God will carry you through these moments of feeling like a failure.

When times like these happen, try looking at the whole picture. Get centered in God's peace. Try not to be so quick to beat yourself up, and remember that every day is a gift. You can never get time back. When I go on a vacation, I vacation!

You have to do what is best for you in any and all situations you face. Don't you want to live in freedom from all that baggage you are carrying around?

Find God's perspective on your life, and let Him empower you to let go of things that are dragging you down. Your body is truly a temple and your mind can become a battlefield if you let it. Shift your perspective every now and then, and watch God strengthen your mind throughout your journey of being healthy.

 Prayer

Lord, I want to see things through Your eyes, not mine. Help me release any negative thoughts and let go of guilt and worry that is keeping me in a stronghold. I want to live a clean and healthy life for You and not anyone else.

Success Lies In The Journey,
Not At The Finish Line

- Kelley Tyan

The Test Is The Testimony

One day back in 2010, I began training for a half marathon. I had never done this before, and to be completely honest, I hated running. My dad, who was an avid runner his whole life, asked me to do this with him, of course I said yes, because it was something we were able to do together and spend time together. When I first started the journey, it was torture. I wanted to quit. I was begging Jesus to let me find a way out.

As the weeks went on, I began to enjoy the runs with my dad. I did not want it to end. I realized the journey is where happiness and success lives. As you are on your own transformation journey, don't forget to enjoy the moments that push you and challenge you along the way. The minute you hit the finish line, it's over.

It is surely a high moment when you finish or accomplish an incredible goal. However, the success and the growth that takes place throughout the journey is where the magic happens, especially in your mind. You realize what you are actually capable of, and you also realize that not giving up and not giving in to the emotional side of it. It will make you mentally stronger.

Through each agonizing long run, I had an opportunity to spend time with my father in a way I never had before. This is what gave me the most pleasure and made me jump out of bed to meet him at the start of a run.

Finishing that half marathon not only brought me closer to my dad, but it also gave me the confidence and the courage to set higher goals for myself. 13.2 miles was definitely a long stretch for me, but I did it. I did it because I changed my mindset about running into a mindset of gratitude for being healthy enough to even run, and I got to celebrate a victory with my dad. Believe it or not, I did it again the following year with him and it was another incredible experience for us.

Starting something new is never easy. Remind yourself that when you are tested, there can be a beautiful testimony that lies ahead of you. Take the chances and bet on yourself, because you only have one shot in life. You cannot take back time.

Prayer

Lord, thank You for giving me the desire and the willingness to keep going even when the road is hard and long. Keep me mentally strong so I can finish what I started no matter what the circumstances are.

Jesus said to him, "If you can believe, all things are possible to him who believes."

- Mark 9:23

Are Your Mind Muscles Weak?

God says all things are possible to those who believe. Have you ever heard, "The mind is a battlefield?" There are certain days where the mind tells so many lies, it can shut a person right down.

Let the Bible verse in Mark speak to you right now. Can you hear God saying, "I believe in you, so why not put your trust and faith in me?"

There are so many days when I don't feel like working out or eating clean. There are so many times when I feel tired, weak, and ready to quit. There are so many moments when I have doubted myself and contemplated stopping my business because I didn't think anyone cared. Have you ever felt that way?

Without those moments, I wouldn't be where I am. Those moments have made me stronger, and I want you to know that God will make things possible for you if you keep going and you keep showing up, while praying along the way.

Whether it's waking up and working out, or being a stay at home mom, or any other . When you get too tired to keep going, rebuild your trust in those moments and believe that all things are possible with Him by your side.

Realize that your inner strength does not always come from you in your humanness.
It can come from God, Who wants to strengthen, equip, and empower you in your weakness.

Every single day, many decisions have to be made: Will I workout? What will I eat to nourish my body? How will I show up today? How will I avoid temptation? And so on...

If you are not constantly strengthening your mind in these areas, it will be weak. You will give in to excuses about not working out, not eating clean, and not showing up the way God wants you to: Happy, strong, beautiful, empowered, capable, and equipped to conquer the day.

Your mind muscles need to be worked on daily to strengthen them, or you will be weak and give in to things you might regret or not be proud of. It is a lifelong process that never stops. There is no finish line when it comes to the strengthening of your mind. It is a day-in-day-out exercise, and when you realize that, you will find your superpower. You will be able to overcome negative thoughts of quitting as well as thoughts that are disrupting your peace.

Are you giving in to your weakness and giving up too easily? God wants to show you how He can and will equip you for the battles in your mind.

Keep working out your mind muscles as well as your physical body, and watch how strong you will become. God believes in you so much that He sent His son to die on a cross for you. All things are possible for you when you have a strong faith, so don't give up so easily. The joy is in the journey of it all.

Lord, today I am giving my mind to You.
I want You to be at the center of all my
thoughts. Give me the strength to overcome
my own excuses that get in the way of being
the person you created me to be: Loving,
beautiful, strong, empowered, and capable.

Eventually all pieces will fall into place. Laugh at the confusion, live for the moment, and know that everything happens for a reason.

- Amy Rees Anderson

Accept That Things Will Be Hard

By now, most of us know and try to understand that life is definitely not easy. In my 47 years of living, I now know that when I am riding the highs of life, I can expect that it might not stay that way forever.

Once I changed my mindset around this concept, I started living life differently.

One day when I was driving home from teaching one of my fitness bootcamp classes, I said to myself, "Life is truly amazing, and I am so grateful and thankful for all God has given me: my husband of my dreams, parents that were the most amazing in the world, and my 2 children."

I was living in that moment and I can vividly remember it, as it still puts a smile on my face.
Guess what happened shortly after that? My mother passed away suddenly. Just when I thought life couldn't get any better, I got sucker-punched in the face.

Now, I don't want you to feel bad right now. I want to empower you to know that life has challenges and will be hard at times, but you will overcome and be able to tell your story or possibly even walk someone else through their pain. Realize that you do not have control over every single thing, and know that only God does. Accept life's challenges as they come your way, and when you pass through the fires and the storms, beautiful things can evolve from them.

Acceptance of anything difficult and different is hard. Change is hard. But when you have faith, God will walk you through all of it. He never said He will help you skip over it or avoid it. He said that He will walk with you, alongside you, and bring you out of it so you can live abundantly again.

There have been many times when I faced challenges that were really hard. There have been times when I would avoid the hard things altogether and bury them deep inside me. (That never works...just saying.) It wasn't until I started accepting and facing the challenges head on, and dealing with my feelings, I could move on and thrive again.

You were born to win and be a fighter through the obstacles and challenges of life. If life were that easy, we would never experience growth in our personal beings.

Once you accept that it's going to be hard, you can work your way through it with God by your side every step of the way. He is the only one Who can give you the peace you need to keep on climbing. Rely fully on this promise, and watch how much stronger you will become along your journey.

Lord, I want to accept the things in life that come my way, good and bad. I know You will walk me through them. Together we will succeed, and we will come out not burned by the fires. My trust is in You, and I will not waiver in that. No matter what happens, I will cling to Your promises of truth to carry me through.

Promise me you'll always remember: you're braver than you believe, stronger than you seem, and smarter than you think.

- Winnie The Pooh

The Faith-Fueled D.O.E.R.S Method

Do you consider yourself a decision maker or are you indecisive at times? Entering my twenties began my indecisiveness. I had a hard time making decisions for myself. The phrase, "should I?" came out of my mouth way too many times each day and at one point, I realized that I was not getting ahead.

I knew I needed to start making strong decisions for myself and stop relying on others because they were not me. I also knew that I needed to start taking action and deciding my own next steps if I wanted to succeed in anything I was doing. By lacking in my decision making process, and not being happy about it, the Faith-Fueled DOERS Method was born.

D: Decide and Disrupt your thought process to make changes where necessary.
O: Organize your thoughts and time.
E: Exercise your mind, body, and spirit daily.
R: Rise above your storms, and Repeat it again.
S: Show up consistently, no matter what or how you feel.

Let me help you change the way you think right now by taking each word one at a time and incorporating the action that goes along with it.

I have realized there are two kinds of people in life: The ones who are the doers, and the ones who stay in the same place, without change.

I am encouraging you to decide to want to grow and take action in an area where you are lacking. At the end of the day, God wants to lead your steps, but you have to start making moves yourself. You can't let others do it for you.

This is where decision making is extremely important. I even see it in my children. They tend to rely on my husband at times, and although that is ok for some instances, we are teaching them to become strong decision makers as they grow into adults.

I want you to grab a dry erase marker and write the word DOER on your bathroom mirror to remind you of who you are and Whose you are. You are a complete and beautiful piece of work in God's eyes, but He also wants you to take control of your life by eliminating things that do not serve you. Whether that is unhealthy foods, friends, jobs, or anything else, make a promise today to start doing things differently.

Here are a few tips:

Become a strong decision maker. Sometimes that means disrupting old thought patterns that are not working anymore. It says in the Bible to let your yes be yes, and your no be no. It doesn't say to be wishy washy.

Organize your time, and wake up earlier if you have to in order to spend time with God. This gives Him space to speak life into you before the day ahead. That is where your fuel should come from.

Schedule movement into your day just like you would a doctor appointment or hair appointment. You know you would NEVER miss a hair appointment, so why not prioritize movement the same way? Your hair will only get you so far...your healthy body will be what gets you to the salon!

Fuel up on His Word or just read one Bible verse if that is all the time you have.

When setbacks occur, say a prayer and know that God will be right by your side through it, no matter what. That is where faith comes in. The storms will come, but we are able to equip ourselves with God's armor. That should give you peace of mind.

Even on your worst days, show up. Show up for YOU, and show up for God, even when no one is looking. By doing this, you will feel accomplished and proud. One thing I know for sure is that on the days when I do not feel like moving my body, those are my best workouts. Take me up on that one.

You can download a free copy of the DOERS Method at www.kelleytyan.com and also listen to the live training I did on my podcast.

Becoming a DOER is a choice! Only you get to decide to stay right where you are or take action and make a change. No matter what your climb looks like, DOING and not STAYING in the same place is the only way you will know if it will succeed.

Lord, I want to be a DOER so I can accomplish all the things you want me to in this life. I am committing today to the DOERS Method, so I can continuously grow and stay on the climb with you by my side.

What you focus on grows, what you think about expands, and what you dwell upon determines your destiny.

– Robin S Sharma

What You Focus On Magnifies!

Every morning my daughter Taylor and I start the day together in the gym. It has been the most sacred part of my days right now because I know they won't last forever. She is working remotely at home after graduating college last Spring, so I am soaking up the time with her as best as I can.

She has grown to love working out over the years, but it always wasn't that way. I never pushed her into it, because I knew it had to come from within her. Thankfully, she has made it one of her priorities now, and she chooses to live a healthy life.

We chat about our progress each day and how strong we feel at times, but at other times, I find the conversation circling around what we don't have. Leaner legs, a 6 pack, bigger muscles, etc.

A coach once told me that whatever I constantly focus on, magnifies. I'll never forget those words. I have made great efforts in many areas of my life trying to focus on the good and the increase I am having, not the bad.

I brought this up to Taylor and explained that, even in the gym, we need to try focusing on the journey and the daily progress, not the things you are wishing for. I tell her to try getting excited to pick up more weights so she can feel stronger each week.

On the days when we are nit-picking about bodies or comparing ourselves to others, we work on bringing our thoughts back to what really matters. Things like the fact that we get to workout. Or how we get to choose clean and healthy foods each day. Also how we get to find new ways to become stronger.

Changing the way you see things is the start of letting go of the negative thoughts. Encouraging each other to be thankful that we are able to workout and do it together at the moment is where the joy comes in.

I remember when I used to focus on the "problem areas" alone, and I never enjoyed the journey of getting stronger. You know what happened then? I pulled out my back and had to stop training completely. Talk about God setting me straight!!

During my resting time, I asked God to slow me down and show me what He wanted me to see. I knew the exact message right away.

If I was going to be my daughter's example of health, I couldn't tear my body apart. Especially since it was the body God gave me. I had to show her how to love and respect her body and use it for the glory of God. As much as we love working out, it takes on a whole different meaning now, for both of us.

In order to be set free of worry, fear that grips you, and uncertainty, you have to give up your control. This is the absolute hardest thing to do for many people, myself included. However, when I stopped trying to control my circumstances, and I gave them all to God, my mind was set free. Peace entered in ways I never dreamed possible.

Prayer

Lord, I am ready to become an example to those around me in health. I am giving my struggles to You, and I am putting my focus on treating my body like a temple that You gave me. Thank You for giving me Your strength so in times I feel weak, You will get me through.

_____

_____

_____

_____

_____

_____

_____

Delight yourself in the Lord, and He will give you the desires of your heart. Commit your ways to the Lord; trust in Him, and He will act.

- *Psalm 37:4-5*

An Almost Person Finishes Last

Do you ever find yourself saying, "I almost finished that project but…" or "I almost got to my weight loss goal but…" or "I almost broke off that bad relationship but they sucked me back in because…"

This list can be extremely long for you right now. Maybe you never thought of it this way before, and I am hoping to open your eyes so you can be more aware of your actions right now. In order to stay on the climb of life in pursuit of health and happiness, the first thing you have to do is acknowledge what you are doing or not doing in the present moment.

Are you almost hitting your weight loss goals, but there always seems to be an excuse in the way? Why does that happen so often? I think being aware of our own actions is the starting place if you really want to make changes.

Do you feel a calling to leave your job and start something new? Maybe you almost left in the past, but you're still there years later. Deciding to be Addicted To The Climb means you are constantly climbing to new heights, even when the times get tough. Leaving a job that you are comfortable in to try something new is extremely hard and challenging, but you will never know if you're good at it until you do that thing.

Praying about a decision like this is the number one answer to get clarity on what you are searching for.

God says in His word in the book of Psalms that He wants you to trust Him fully, and He will give you the desires of your heart. This is where you really have to put your trust and faith in God to take those next steps, instead of almost taking them.

Every single day in my own business, I have to put faith in God because sometimes I am weak. I try to let God always lead the way and be the CEO of my life in business, because I cannot do everything myself or else I will never finish. I will be almost finishing what I start, and that's not where I want to be. I know you don't want to be an "almost - kind of" person either. What if I almost finished this book, but never did?!

If you are an almost person and you never finish what you start, God can't take you to higher places.
Realize that the journey to get from point A to point B is sometimes very challenging and hard. There are always going to be bumps along the way, but it's not about the finish line. It's about enjoying the journey and seeing all the changes that take place along the way.

I remember when I was running my first half marathon; the training was so intense. There were so many moments when I wanted to quit, because I hated the long runs. In the end, all those long runs made me stronger in my mind. When I look back, it wasn't about finishing the race. It was about all the memories of the long runs that I am cherishing and the challenges I faced along the way. It was about all the times I wanted to quit, but I didn't. I wanted to prove to myself that if I could just get through one more run I'd be so proud of myself, and that's what I did.

If you keep almost finishing tasks and quitting, what stories will you have to tell in the end? I have found that the more I welcome challenging times, the more they become greater opportunities to trust God. God tells us that no set of circumstances is too much for us to handle. He also says that it is through trials that we become stronger. It is through pain that we can find our purpose.

Even in my own business, there were many times where I started creating a new program and almost gave up because I didn't think anyone would be interested in it. I didn't want to be embarrassed to put something out there and not have anyone like it. I especially didn't want someone to buy the program and not get results. If I had quit, what would happen to the hundreds of lives that were transformed through those programs?

I want you to think about all the things that you set out to do and haven't finished yet because things got too hard for you. I want you to choose one or two of those things, and start again. You are much stronger than you think, and quitting will never get you where you want to go. It only brings on feelings of guilt! No one wants that! Put on your armor of God today, and become unstoppable. Let's take the phrase "I almost" out of the equation and add in "I completed!"

Think how proud of yourself you will be when you complete something that is so meaningful to you, and you did it even through difficulties.

Don't give up on yourself. Let's stay on the climb together, and remember, when you reach a new mountain top there's always another mountain to climb. Life is all about the climb, because if we stayed on a flat surface forever it would be extremely boring.

I always say when you climb one flight of stairs and you are tired, use the platform as a launching pad. Take your rest for a few moments and then start back up again.

What mountain are you ready to start climbing again? I would love to hear from you. God is waiting to take those next steps with you, and walk side by side, helping you finish what you started.

Prayer

Lord, I am excited to finish what I start and not grow weary, because I have You by my side. Help me to stay on the climb no matter what or who tries to stop me. Thank You for giving me the strength to keep on climbing.

For we are God's masterpiece. He has created us anew in Christ Jesus, so that we can do the good things He planned for us long ago.

- Ephesians 2:10

The War Within

Are you guilty of body shaming yourself? What about thinking you are less than? Have you ever wanted to change the way you look or change a specific area of your body? I can answer yes to all those questions personally. In all honesty, it has been a long and antagonizing road of feeling unworthy, shameful, and all the negative feelings that come along with thinking these things. Come to find out, this way of thinking starts for many girls before 10 years old!

I want to change the way we think starting today! Let's start working on our minds in a brand new way.

The war that rages inside of us is absolutely real and alive, because we know that the devil himself is always trying to tear us down. If anyone ever tells you to just "get over it" and stop "being so hard on yourself," then good for them and be happy they are not dealing with these feelings.

However, for many women out there, including myself, I have battled with "keeping up" for far too long. I am ready to win the war that rages in my mind, and I want to lock arms with you too.
I always asked myself, "Why am I letting this go on?" I deeply know God created me and you beautiful and unique, but there's one important thing to remember: There is a devil that is always ready and waiting to devour

anyone that is feeling weak or less than. In fact, those are his favorite targets!

Most women feel guilty of this behavior from time to time, and maybe that's you right now. God didn't create us to feel this way ever! Unfortunately, somewhere along the way we were told we don't look good enough, pretty enough, skinny enough, and so on.

I know for me, it started when I was a little girl reading magazines. I was obsessed with how women looked in magazines. From the time I was seven years old, and I wanted to be perfect because they looked perfect. Little did I know, back then that they were airbrushed to look that way. I thought that's what women were supposed to look like.

Can you relate? It took me years of tearing myself apart to try to keep up, and I can tell you firsthand that I lost years off my life fighting against myself. It was completely exhausting.

Now that my daughter is grown up, and I have grown up, I have taken this matter very seriously. I do not ever want to go back to that mentality again. God is the only one Who can reveal to you what you truly look like: A beautiful masterpiece, if you are willing to see yourself through His eyes. That is exactly what I had to start doing.

If you struggle in this area, it is time you face it and do something about it. It's not fair for you to go through life feeling this way. Let's talk about the way we work out and why we work out. If you are working out for vanity reasons, you will never reach your goal, ever.

Believe me, it does not work because even if you do reach your goal, you will never visibly see it on yourself. Think about a time when you lost weight. Maybe it was 10, 20, or 30 pounds, and you felt great. Did you still pick yourself apart as if you didn't lose the weight?

Don't you want to relieve some of the pressure you put on yourself and let God take it from you? He stands over you every single time you look in the mirror wondering why you pick apart the unique body He created specifically for you. Now flip the switch to your nutrition. What are you eating that is making you feel good and healthy day to day?

God definitely does not want us eating junk and treating our bodies carelessly. He wants us to eat God-made foods so we can feel Incredible each day. The only way to feel incredible is when we feed our bodies the right way, and not with processed foods, white sugars, or lots of sodium. All of that makes us angry inside whether we realize it or not.

Food is definitely our mood, and what we eat is what we become. Your mind is tied into the food you eat, and when you are eating healthy and feeling good in your body, you are much happier! A happier version of yourself is so much better. Am I right?

If you are fighting a war inside you, start with the food you are eating and start with noticing how much movement you are doing within the week. What are you doing to help yourself? Or, are you sitting comfortable in that misery?

I heard someone say that many women think of their

bodies as a prison. I want to ask you, how are you going to get yourself out of that space? Then you can live freely with God by your side as his daughter who loves you and created you flawless in His eyes.

We are not competing with other people; it always comes down to our own thoughts about ourselves. You can decide today to keep living in misery inside these prison walls, or you can change something. Maybe change the way you eat so you can feel better. Don't change for vanity reasons, but just to feel better.

I want you to take your power back right now instead of letting yourself get stripped of it. You have everything inside you to flourish, because God made you perfect. But it is up to you to choose to live in that and not try to live up to what the world's standards are.

I fall short of this myself, but I know I am a work in progress. Little by little, I have been working on this. It feels so much better and so much more freeing than being inside the four wall prison cell of my head.

Are you truly ready to let go, and let God in?

Lord, I realize there is a spiritual war going on inside my head. I want to end this today, and I am asking You to help me see myself through Your eyes. I know You love me and have created me a masterpiece. I don't ever want to take that for granted, and I want to be a light so others can see them- selves through Your eyes too.

Check In

Remember those goals we set at the beginning of this book? Have they changed at all since you finished reading?

Today I am *staying on the climb* and committing to:

_____

_____

_____

Today, _____

is a *non-negotiable,* and I will stay committed.

I promise myself that *today* I will be

_____

_____

_____

Closing

stay Addicted to the Climb

I want to thank you for reading this book, and I pray you have had a renewing of your mind and a rebirth of your spirit through these pages and stories.

The stories in this book were meant to encourage and empower you to become mentally, emotionally, and spiritually stronger.

God will never leave you nor forsake you! So in everything you do, do it for the glory of God. Remind yourself that you will never be perfect and you will always be a work in progress. You can be kind to yourself and forgiving as you are journeying through life and embracing every new Climb.

Through every step back, there is always a stronger comeback! As you are climbing up your own mountain, keep looking ahead, because everything is going to always work out if you keep on climbing. In the moments where you want to quit or give up, look up to the heavens and God will give you strength.

Three final words I want you to put on repeat in your mind:

YOU ARE *Enough*

God created you perfect, without a blemish. I want you to know how proud He is of you! Your job and focus is to keep getting back up on your feet, because every time you fall, you will become stronger.

There is one thing I know for sure and that is: This girl loves you!

XO, Kelley

Let Kelley know how her book impacted you!

Visit Amazon to leave a review.

Tag @kelleytyan on Instagram to share a journal page, favorite quote, or eye-opening moment.

Join Kelley's private Facebook group for women on the climb! You can find the link on www.kelleytyan.com.

Visit www.kelleytyan.com to learn when the next Addicted To The Climb book club is starting!

Addicted to the Climb Podcast

Follow Kelley's podcast, all about faith-led fitness, health. and mindset transformation for women over 40. It's available everywhere, including Apple Podcasts and Spotify!

Kelley Tyan

Kelley Tyan is a master transformation coach for women in faith, fitness, and mindset. She is a 4X national bikini champion, breast cancer survivor, host of her podcast show, Addicted To The Climb, and author. She is also a proud wife and mother of her 2 children.

She has been blessed to be featured on ABC, local radio shows, and many publications for her work on empowering and inspiring women to live healthy and fit lives. She is the founder of the Level Up live event, because she believes that building a strong and powerful community of women who want to stay on the climb of life is her mission. She invites those who are searching for more to join her private

Facebook community called Faith, Fuel, and Fitness.

Through years of her own work on self-development, she has coached and transformed the lives of many women in mind, body, and soul. She has realized that there is only one thing you can count on in this life; there's always going to be another mountain to climb, it's how you decide to take the first step.

Kelley is continuously committed to empowering women through her accountability coaching programs, and her greatest advice is to never stop climbing, because every climb you take will make you stronger for the next one.

Extra Journaling Space

Manufactured by Amazon.ca
Bolton, ON

27519325R00111